W9-AAF-224

THE
STORY OF
GRAVITY

by Germaine Beiser

THE STORY OF GRAVITY
THE STORY OF THE EARTH'S MAGNETIC FIELD

by Germaine and Arthur Beiser

THE STORY OF COSMIC RAYS
PHYSICS FOR EVERYBODY

THE STORY OF GRAVITY

An Historical Approach to the Study of the Force That Holds the Universe Together

diagrams by George H. Buehler

E. P. DUTTON & CO., INC.
NEW YORK

Published simultaneously in Canada by Clarke, Irwin & Company Limited, Toronto and Vancouver.

Library of Congress Catalog Card Number: 68–24718

First Edition

CONTENTS

To the memory of my father

THE STORY OF GRAVITY

INTRODUCTION

The trouble with learning about gravity is that it is too familiar. It was the first force you felt, the first to which you were formally introduced—perhaps even in kindergarten. Your teacher decided to make sure that her charges learned science early. "What makes things fall down?" she asked. "Gravity," you pronounced proudly, feeling a nice warm glow. Your teacher felt a nice warm glow too, and you both felt that there was no more to say about that subject. There *is* a bit more to learn about gravity, however, as you will find out on reading this book.

It may seem hard to believe that all the forces so far known to scientists can be classified into four fundamental types. The first two come as no surprise: gravitational forces and electromagnetic forces. The remaining two forces describe other interactions between nuclear particles; they are called, respectively, the strong nuclear force and the weak interaction. (True, there are chemical forces, muscular forces, mechanical forces, and so on, but all of these can be reduced to the fundamental four.) Of these four forces by far the weakest is gravity.

Now let us go on to learn about this weakest of forces, the force that nevertheless holds together the universe.

chapter one — *THE TRIUMPH OF THE SUN*

A fact that we take for granted is that the *same* force harnesses the planets and makes bodies fall to the earth. This certainty is a recent one. Mankind went along for hundreds of thousands of years making all sorts of observations and discoveries before someone made the really not-so-very-obvious connection between motion on earth and motion in space. It was Galileo Galilei who first suspected that there was but one law operating. Galileo set forth the first equation of gravitation, but he was able to prove it valid only on earth. Later Isaac Newton was able to fuse the planetary laws of Johann Kepler and the work of Galileo into the statement of a *universal* law of gravitation.

Could Newton have made his pronouncement if he had been born in an earlier time when men thought that the *earth* was the center of the heavens? It is very doubtful that even so great a genius as Newton could have seen through the tangle of wheels within wheels by which the early philosophers represented the motions of the planets to find the underlying gravitational attractive force. A sun-centered solar system was essential to Newton's work. To trace the development of the theory of gravity we must go back to an earlier time when the existence of gravity as a force was not even suspected. We begin with the history of the sun-centered or Copernican theory.

Pythagoras

All primitive civilizations have found explanations of the path followed every day across the sky by the sun, of the slow changing of the stars' positions which brings them back to their starting point in a year's time, of the wanderings of the planets. Gods and great animals play important roles in these schemes which are, alas, not relevant to this story of gravity. We begin our history a little later, in the sixth century B.C. By this time the Greeks had produced thinkers who, discarding the gods, sought explanations that could be reached by logical thought. One of these men was Pythagoras of Samos who made a sort of religion of measurement. Pythagoras gave such importance to numbers that he suspected they made up the basic stuff of the universe! Much of his work was correct—he is responsible for the Pythagorean Theorem, for example—but he made the mistake common to all the ancient Greeks of believing that the truth can be reached by thought alone. This arrogant attitude was the cause of his mistakes in the field of astronomy. The theories Pythagoras proposed were certainly reasonable, logical conclusions to draw from what he saw in the skies. Unfortunately, he did not see enough; his ideas were based on too few observations, and they were, for the most part, wrong. Sad to say,

Pythagoras' theories of celestial motion went more or less unchallenged for the next two thousand years. Pythagoras rejected the belief that the earth is a cylinder on whose flat top we live and suggested that instead it is a floating sphere. But this step forward was canceled by his theory that the sun circles the earth once a year while the *whole sky,* including the sun, is carried around the earth every day on a rotating hollow sphere. The plane of the sun's path was set at an angle to that of the direction of rotation of the sky, just as in Figure 1–1. With this scheme Pythagoras could explain the rising and setting of the sun, and because of the angle between the planes, he could also account for the changing positions on the horizon of the rising and setting sun.

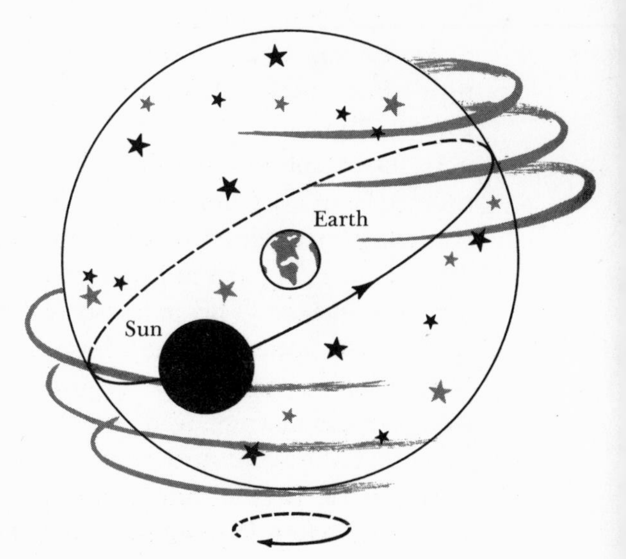

Figure 1–1. The sphere of the sky rotating once a day about the earth, carrying with it the sun which moves once a year about the earth.

Aristotle

Years later, in 384 B.C., Aristotle was born. He became the tutor to Alexander the Great of Macedonia, who went on to conquer most of the known world and to spread Greek civilization wherever he went. As a result Aristotle, who was famous as a philosopher in Greece, became known the world over. His ideas gained an importance that they might not otherwise have had. As it happened, Aristotelian thought, translated by Jewish scholars into Arabic, was later introduced by the Moslems into Europe, where it was eventually translated into Latin. Absorbed and transformed by St. Thomas Aquinas, Aristotle's ideas became part of Christian theology. In this form Aristotle's philosophy reached across the centuries to hamper Copernicus, Bruno, and Galileo among many others in their freedom of thought.

Aristotle's ideas were numerous, so let us mention only those which held back the development of the theory of gravity. Aristotle imagined the universe to be a series of spheres within spheres. Outside the outermost sphere was nothing at all; the innermost sphere was the earth, which was motionless. The other spheres moved, carrying around with them the sun, the planets, and the moon. The stars were stuck into the outer sphere; the sphere of the moon acted as an important separation between the region of the earth, where things could change, and the regions beyond, where all was unchangeable and perfect. Aristotle imagined the circle to be better than a straight line since the line must stop when it reaches a boundary whereas a circle never stops but continues forever on itself. For this reason, said Aristotle, the motions outside the moon's sphere must be on circular paths. Another theory that seemed obvious to Aristotle was that on earth heavy bodies fall faster than light ones. These were some of the false ideas that philosophers had to overcome years later.

The Ptolemaic System

You must not imagine that absolutely no one disagreed with Aristotle's picture of the planetary motion. In fact, in Aristotle's own time a fellow Greek named Heraclides suggested that the strange movements of Venus and Mercury, which stay close to the sun and are seen sometimes on one side of the sun and sometimes on the other, could be explained if these two planets circled the sun instead of the earth. Heraclides did not go farther; in his scheme the sun, with Venus and Mercury, revolved about the earth. In the next century, however, another Greek astronomer, Aristarchus of Samos, took the idea farther to propose that perhaps the other known planets—Mars, Jupiter, and Saturn—also circled the sun. He then boldly pointed out that the yearly progression of the stars could be explained as well if the *earth* also circled the sun, instead of vice versa. Aristarchus also explained the rising and setting of the sun by suggesting that the earth turns once a day on its axis. Unfortunately this early Copernican did not take the trouble to show in detail the agreement between his theory and the actual motions of the heavenly bodies. With nothing solid to back it up, Aristarchus' theory was soon forgotten. Moreover, in the next century Hipparchus of Rhodes gave his earth-centered theory substantial support by using it to compute tables predicting the future positions of the planets. The famous Ptolemy of Alexandria continued this work and then included it in his encyclopedia of astronomy called the *Almagest.* This book was compiled in A.D. 150 and translated into Latin during the Dark Ages—a gift of knowledge from the past to an awakening Europe. The earth-centered theory endorsed by Ptolemy was launched across the centuries by the *Almagest* and thus acquired Ptolemy's name. Bolstered by Aristotle's reputation, the Ptolemaic theory became accepted as the truth by Renaissance Europe.

Problems with the Ptolemaic System

You might be curious about the kind of calculations that astronomers such as Hipparchus and Ptolemy could make to support a theory that claims that the *earth* is the center of the universe. It does take some rather fancy tinkering to justify the Ptolemaic system, but it can be done. Before we investigate how this is accomplished, let us survey the information that these astronomers had to work with.

The five visible planets are Jupiter, Saturn, Mars, Venus, and Mercury. We can observe their paths, and those of the sun, the moon, and a remarkable number

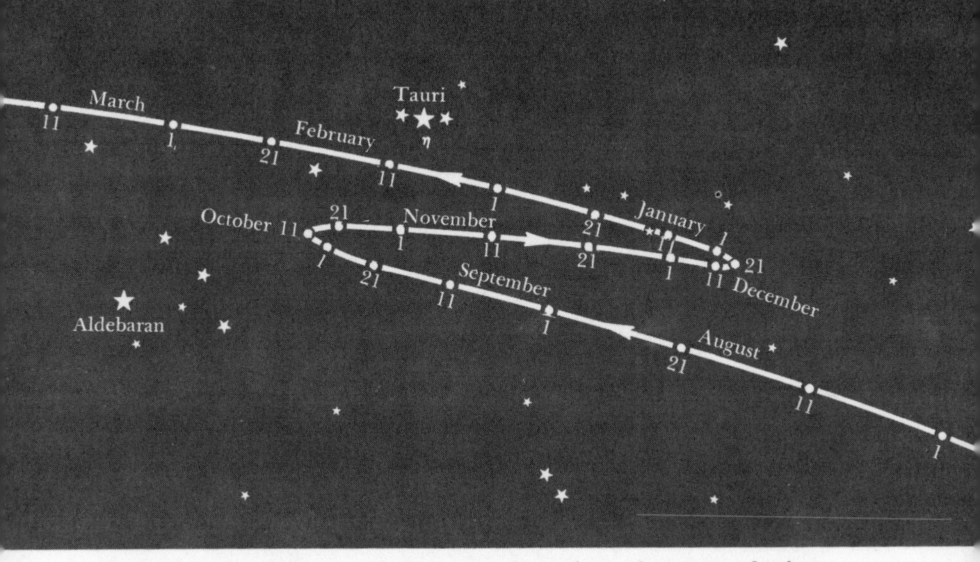

Figure 1–2. Mars as it appeared against the stars during August through March of a certain year. Notice the "retrograde" motion from October 11 to December 21.

of stars all without the help of the telescope. If we could only stand somewhere beyond the solar system to watch the whole conglomeration working like a mechanical toy it would be obvious what is going on. It is our misfortune that we must watch the action from the earth. From here it is not at all obvious that the planets are going around the sun; this is what gave the old astronomers so much trouble. What we do see if we watch a planet for a period of time is a very peculiar path. For example, what path do we see Mars follow? A circle, an ellipse, or even a spiral? No. Let us begin to observe Mars at a time when Earth and Mars are moving in the same direction and Mars is a little bit ahead. We fix Mars's position using the distant stars for reference. From Figure 1–2 you can see that the apparent position of Mars against the stars changes as time goes on. At first it seems to be moving forward with respect to the stars, but then there comes a time when it appears to have stopped! At the next observation we can see that Mars has actually gone backward with respect to the stars. It almost seems as though the planet cannot make up its mind; you can understand why "planet" means "wanderer." Seen from the earth the paths of the planets look like Figure 1–3.

These sometimes direct and sometimes "retrograde" motions do not give much support to the Aristotelian

Figure 1–3. The paths of the planets known in Ptolemy's time as they appear *from the earth.* The orbits of the planets describe loops while the sun and the moon perform simple circles about the earth.

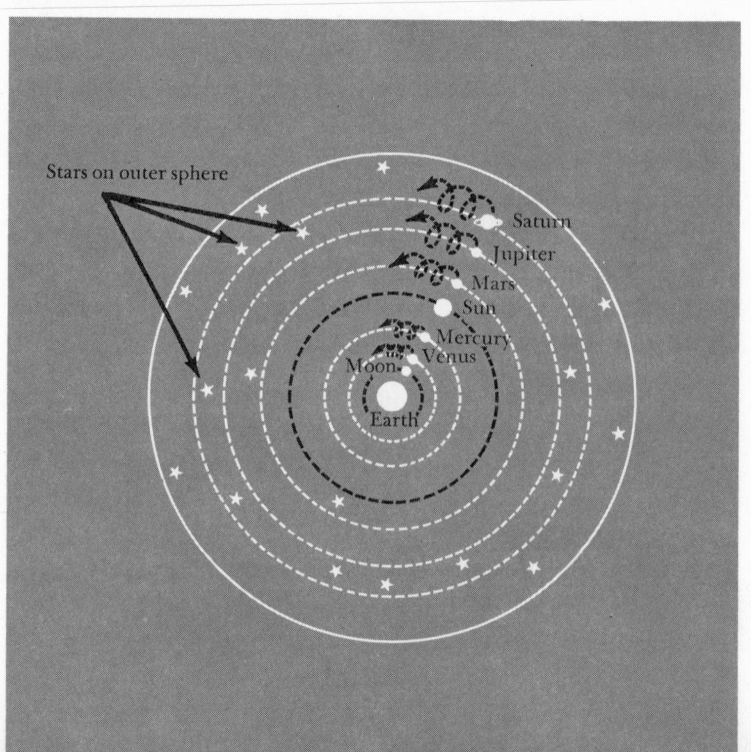

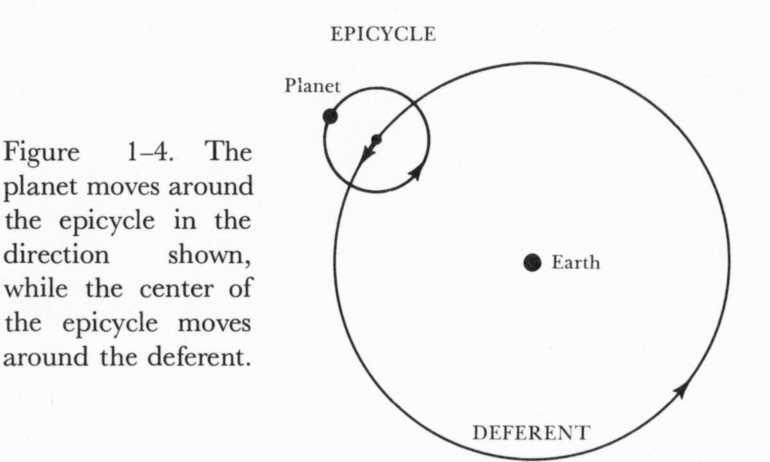

Figure 1–4. The planet moves around the epicycle in the direction shown, while the center of the epicycle moves around the deferent.

idea that planets move in simple circles or that they move with a constant speed. It is not only Mars that moves in this strange fashion; the other planets also misbehave and cannot be seen to move in circular orbits about the earth. It is only the sun that seems to move around us before our eyes. We are about to see how philosophers such as Hipparchus and Ptolemy were able to explain what anyone could see in the skies, and yet maintain the theory that the planets moved in circles at constant speed and that they moved about the earth.

Making the Ptolemaic System Work

The justification of the Ptolemaic system was accomplished with the help of two devices called the *epicycle* and the *deferent*. The planet in this scheme moved about the little circle, the epicycle, in the direction shown in Figure 1–4. Meanwhile the epicycle was moving around the larger track, the deferent, at whose center lay the earth. By combining these two motions and adjusting the relative sizes of the two circles and the relative speeds around the circles, all sorts of paths can be made to order. It was possible to produce a path like that of Figure 1–3, for example. As Mars moved around the imaginary epicycle, seen from the earth it would appear sometimes to be moving to the right, sometimes to the left, to agree with the observations of Mars's behavior.

For each planet there was a separate epicycle and a separate deferent. The circles were of different sizes; the epicycles moved at different speeds around the deferents and the planets moved at different speeds around their epicycles. Thus a very good approximation to the observed motion of the planets could be fabricated while maintaining the fiction that the planets moved in circles at constant speed around the earth. But even this complicated system did not agree *completely* with the observations of the astronomers. The scheme was successively patched up through the ages as epicycles were added to epicycles to fit new data. The result was an intricate conglomeration of wheels within wheels. It worked, but it was not beautiful. The concept of beauty based on simplicity of a theory is very important to the scientist. At times this intuitive, semiartistic approach can lead the scientist astray, but it still plays a great role in his thinking.

By now you have realized that the theory that the planets move around the earth is not so fantastic after all! Indeed, the planets whose paths lie outside the earth's path do go around the earth (in a way) while going around the sun. But the artificiality introduced to make the earth, and not the sun, the center of motion of the solar system assures that any fundamental laws of motion will lie hidden in the tangle. A new and simpler system was needed; it was provided around the turn of the sixteenth century by Nicolas Copernicus.

Nicolas Copernicus

Nicolas Copernicus was born in the year 1473 in what is now Poland. The name Copernicus is a Latin version of his real name, which may have been of German origin. On the death of his father, Nicolas was adopted by his maternal uncle, a wealthy bishop who sent his nephew to the University of Cracow. There was then a celebrated school of astronomy at Cracow, whose main reason for being was to keep the Church calendar in order. A formidable problem for those astronomers was adapting the existing calendar to give better predictions of such basic occurrences as the times of the full moons and of the vernal equinox, which is the first day of spring. Feasts such as Easter Sunday were tied to these happenings. The work of the Cracow astronomers aroused Copernicus' interest. While he was still a college student Copernicus came to the conclusion that it was the motion of the earth, and not of the sun, that was responsible for sunrise and sunset. As the earth was commonly believed to stand still, to postulate a rotation of the earth on its axis was very daring. It may have been as early as this period that Copernicus realized that the movements of the planets would appear much simpler if we regarded the *sun* instead of the earth as the center of motion. Once he had accepted that the earth could move at all, it was not so difficult for Copernicus to imagine that the earth could move around the sun. At this point Copernicus had no calculations to back up his ideas, no proof that he was right. Between the brilliant theories of a young genius and the completed and closely reasoned statements that made up his book, *De Revolutionibus,* lay a lifetime of astronomical work.

Developing a New Theory

The bishop next sent his nephew to study in Italy, the country where the Renaissance began, and to which the best scholars of that time were drawn. At the University of Bologna the spirit of free discussion was in the air. One of the topics that had Copernicus' sympathy concerned attempts to describe the universe in terms of geometry with the hope of simplifying the old Ptolemaic system. The Bolognese astronomers reinforced Copernicus' belief that the simplest theory is the best. Copernicus passed ten years in Italy, studying law and taking a degree in it, studying medicine and Greek, indulging in his astronomical fancies and his more frivolous ones as well.

During his absence, Copernicus' uncle had arranged

for him to become a canon of Frauenburg Cathedral near the present-day Polish-Russian border. The young canon was excused from his duties, first to continue his studies in Italy and later to act as his uncle's private physician. By 1512 when he at last took up his responsibilities in Frauenburg (fifteen years after his appointment), Copernicus had had ample time to develop and organize his astronomical ideas. He set them forth in a tract circulated among his friends in that year.

At Frauenburg Copernicus installed himself and an observatory in one of the turrets of the fortified cathedral's wall. From this romantic aerie Copernicus made many observations of the skies—all of them, sad to say, not quite accurate enough. Copernicus then set about working these measurements plus the also incorrect records of other astronomers into the framework of his new planetary system, determining the orbits of the planets and the radii of the "circles" they described around the sun. A job that would be hard enough anyway was made even more difficult by Copernicus' belief in the accuracy of his data. Another problem was that Copernicus never realized that the planetary orbits are elliptical, not circular, a difference that affects the calculations of their orbits. It is amazing that with these handicaps Copernicus kept his faith fixed on the simplicity of the sun-centered theory. It is not so surprising to find that Copernicus could not make the details of his system agree exactly with observation so that he was forced at last to resort to the same epicycles that marred the Ptolemaic system.

De Revolutionibus

You should not have the impression that Copernicus' astronomical observations were wildly inaccurate. The fact is simply that they did not meet the exact standards needed for plotting the paths of the planets precisely. For example, he calculated the distance of the moon as 60.30 times the earth's radius, as opposed to the modern-day value of 60.37. Copernicus gave the radius of Mars's orbit as 1.520 times the radius of the earth's orbit instead of today's value of 1.524, and Jupiter's orbital radius as 5.219 instead of 5.203. Copernicus' value for the *star year* (the time taken by the sun to complete its apparent cycle among the stars and return to its starting point) was only thirty seconds greater than our value. As a by-product of this work Copernicus was able to suggest changes in the Church calendar, recommendations that were adopted forty years after his death by Pope Gregory XIII to form the Gregorian calendar that we use today.

The Reformation made the Roman Catholic Church wary of new ideas, while the newly formed Lutheran Church tended to interpret the Bible literally. Because of these religious sensitivities Copernicus had made no great effort to propagate his ideas, theories that would have been considered irrelevant to religion a few years earlier. Nevertheless, the 1512 tract had attracted many disciples who wanted to learn more about this novel way of looking at the universe. In 1540 Copernicus allowed a student to publish a summary of his ideas in a work called *First Account.* He at last decided to allow the entire manuscript, the work of thirty years, to be published. This masterpiece, never titled by Copernicus, is known as *De Revolutionibus Orbium Coelestium (On the Revolutions of the Heavenly Spheres).* Copernicus received the completed book several weeks before his death on May 24, 1543.

Despite its flaws, *De Revolutionibus* offered its readers a concept of beautiful simplicity. Sad to say, simplicity was the only advantage it could offer over the Ptolemaic system. A choice between two systems of planetary motion, both based on insufficient and inaccurate observations, was no choice at all. The world needed a man who would devote his life to making superaccurate measurements of the wanderings of the planets. Luckily there was such a man. His name was Tycho Brahe, born three years after Copernicus' death.

chapter two ELLIPSE

You must be wondering by now what the last chapter has to do with gravity. The answer is that the Copernican theory is essential to prepare the way for a theory of gravity. It is doubtful that Sir Isaac Newton, brilliant though he was, could have formulated his law of universal gravitation if he had been confined by the Ptolemaic system. Newton's gravity was a force that depended (in a way we shall talk about later) on the distance from a *center of force.* The simplicity of the Copernican theory in which motion was symmetrical about a center was needed before the law of gravity could be revealed.

Two men linked Copernicus and Newton; they were Tycho Brahe and Johann Kepler. Tycho Brahe, by producing a really accurate and complete set of data, made possible the discovery by his student Johann Kepler that the planetary orbits are not after all circular, but elliptical. From Kepler's laws Newton was able to deduce his own laws of gravitation.

Tycho Brahe

Tycho Brahe was born of noble parents in Denmark in 1546. From his studies in various universities in northern Europe, Brahe emerged with a great interest in astronomy. One fact that impressed him was the inaccuracy of the existing tables of planetary motion. It would be very difficult, Brahe realized, to construct a proper theory of the planets with poor data. In 1572 a new star, or *nova,* suddenly appeared in the skies, so bright that it could be seen in daylight. Such sudden flare-ups of existing stars are no mystery to astronomers today, but that sixteenth-century nova caused quite a sensation by casting doubt on Aristotle's belief that nothing new could spring up among the stars. If, on the other hand, this nova were close enough to the earth, then its changeability disturbed no theory. Much, then, depended on the distance from the nova to the earth, and with a paper on this subject Brahe attracted the attention of the reigning King Frederick. The king, a patron of the arts and sciences, was quick to lend Brahe his support. This took the form of the whole island of Hven, which lies a bit north of Copenhagen in the Sound between Denmark and Sweden, along with funds to set up an astronomical observatory there. With this superb ancestor of the government grant, Brahe made himself a little kingdom, complete with two observatories, one underground so that his delicate instruments would not be affected by vibrations. He also set up a paper mill, printing press, laboratories, museum, library, and even a jail—everything the "compleat scientist" might need for his comfort! To this establishment came scholars from all over Europe.

Brahe spent the next twenty years making accurate observations of the stars and the planets. Among his accomplishments were an extensive star catalog, giving the positions of many stars, and a long series of observations of the movements of the planet Mars. Lacking the telescope (which had yet to be invented), Brahe was still able to make remarkably precise determinations of the star and planet positions, partly because he must have been an extraordinarily careful man, blessed with excellent eyesight, but also through his invention of the sextant. This instrument, a modification of Copernicus' quadrant, is really very simple. It consists essentially of two arms with a protractor between them as shown in Figure 2–1. One arm is fixed, the other free to move. The observer, looking through sights attached to the movable arm, raises this arm until the star is in view through the sight; he then records the angle that appears on the protractor. The maximum angle that the arm of Brahe's instrument could reach was 60°, hence its name of "sextant." It was a simple device, but a scarcely more sophisticated version is still in use as a basic instrument of navigation.

It is hardly surprising that during all those years

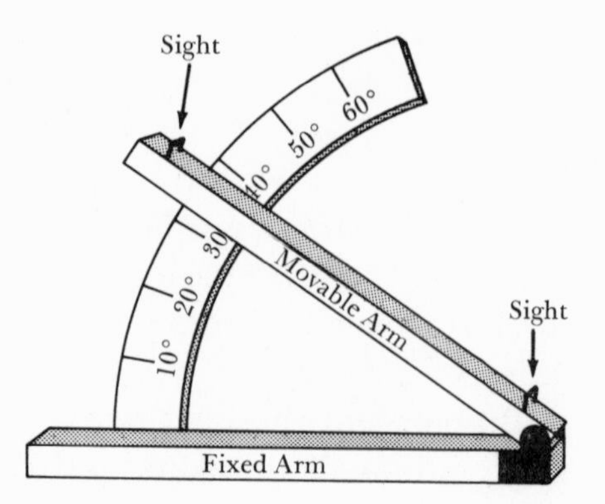

Figure 2–1. Tycho Brahe's sextant.

spent accumulating so many measurements Brahe wondered about their meaning. On the one hand he admired the simplicity of Copernicus' theory; on the other, he could not believe that the earth could move. Brahe's compromise was a system in which the planets circled the sun, while the sun together with the moon circled the earth.

A few years after the great king Christian IV succeeded his father, the scientific idyll on the isle of Hven came to an end. Brahe, a crotchety man, could not get along with the new king. Christian took back Brahe's pleasure dome and forbade him to work in Copenhagen. Brahe went into self-exile in Prague where, before he could begin to work, he died in 1601. The only fruit of his stay in Prague was the training of a young assistant, Johann Kepler. The bad luck that made poor Brahe an exile at his death was the world's good fortune, for it was this move that put Brahe's records into the hands of the man who would give the work enormous significance, Johann Kepler.

Johann Kepler

Unlike Copernicus and Brahe, Kepler was born (in 1571 in Germany) into a poor and not even respectable family. His father was an alcoholic, and his mother was at one time tried for being a witch. Nevertheless Kepler won a scholarship to the University of Tübingen, where he was very much influenced by the Copernican ideas of the Professor of Mathematics. On graduating from the university, Kepler took a position as a teacher in Graz, where he had much free time which he used to speculate on astronomical problems. A book setting forth some of his ideas (incorrect ones, as it turned out) caught Brahe's attention. In 1599, when Brahe came to Prague, he asked Kepler to join him as his assistant, and Kepler was happy to do so.

A few years later Kepler inherited Brahe's observations, but not his instruments. Kepler himself was not rich enough to buy or have made equally good equipment. Circumstances forced him to do what talent especially fitted him for: to find a fundamental scheme that would agree with this great mass of correct measurements. The first task was to find some simple formula that would describe the orbit of Mars and that would agree with Brahe's observations. At first Kepler worked along traditional lines. He tried to find a combination of *circular* paths that would make up a theoretical orbit that passed through the points where Brahe had actually observed the planet. After four years of mathematical drudgery Kepler was successful in concocting a path that fitted the observed motion of Mars so well that the two orbits, theoretical and real, never appeared farther apart than one quarter of a full moon (or, really, the angle subtended by that segment of the moon). At this point you might forgive Kepler for sitting back with a self-congratulatory sigh. He did not.

We now have come to a turning point in the history of science, one in its way as important as Kepler's Laws themselves. Kepler was so certain that Brahe's figures were right that he rejected a theory that did not fit

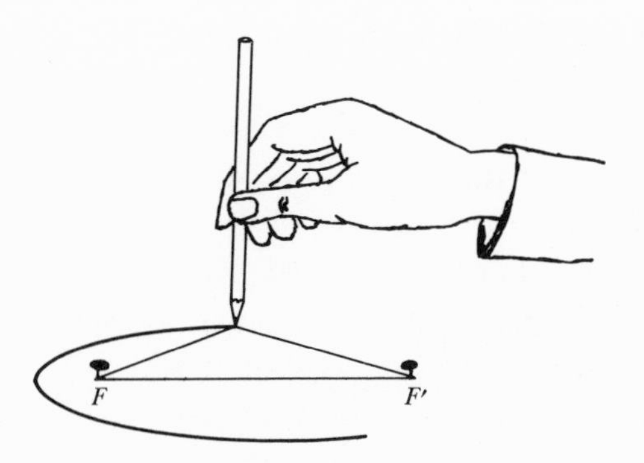

Figure 2–2. Drawing an ellipse.

these numbers *exactly*. The data could not be made to agree with circular orbits; therefore Kepler went on working until, after testing and rejecting seventy hypotheses (!), he did find a curve that fit the data. To his surprise it was an *ellipse* with the sun at one focus. Instead of cutting the data to fit the theory Kepler cut the theory to fit the data. Here was the prelude to modern science!

The Ellipse

An ellipse is not just any old egg-shaped curve. It can be described by formulas in several ways that specify its shape. Each point on an ellipse is *where* it is in obedience to the formula for that particular ellipse. Imagine that you wish to draw an ellipse. Pick two points on a piece of paper as in Figure 2–2 and label them F and F'. Stick a tack in each point and then pass a loop of thread (of length greater than twice the distance between the tacks) over the tacks. Now if you hold the point of a pencil against the thread and, keeping the thread taut, trace a line wherever the thread allows you to go, the curve you draw will be an ellipse. You will find that the pencil, reined in by the length of the thread and the position of the pins, can draw *only* an ellipse, and its shape and size will depend on the length of the thread and the separation of the tacks. The long axis of the ellipse is called the *major axis;* it is customarily labeled $2a$. The points F and F' are called the *foci* of the ellipse. By changing the length of the string or the separation of the tacks you can draw ellipses of different sizes and shapes. For example, if the thread is only twice as long as the distance between tacks, the pencil can draw only a straight line. If the tacks are not separated at all, the ellipse you draw will be a circle. A circle and a straight line are the extreme cases of an ellipse—you can find examples of all shapes in between, as you see in Figure 2–3.

Kepler's First Two Laws

Naturally Kepler wondered if other planets than Mars followed elliptical paths. He found

Figure 2–3. Ellipses of various shapes. The planetary orbits are very nearly circular.

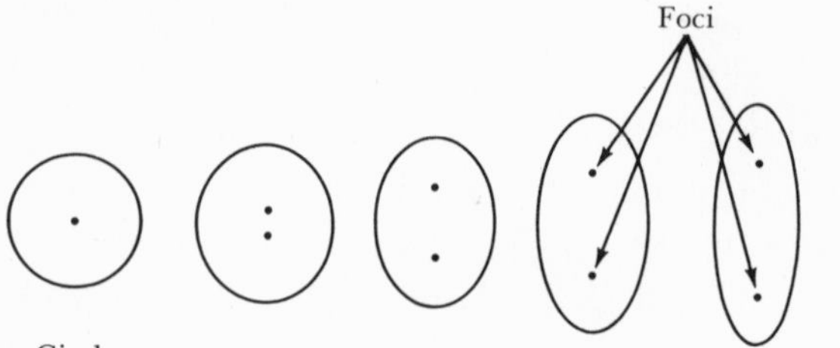

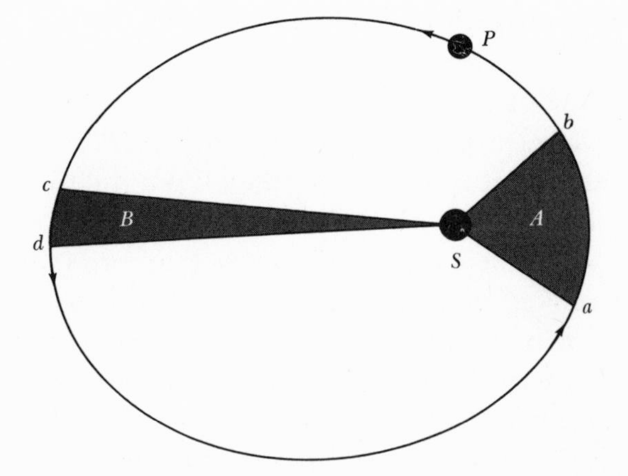

Figure 2–4. Planet *P* moving around sun *S*. Area *A* is swept out as planet goes from *a* to *b* during a certain time interval. Area *B* is swept out as the planet goes from *c* to *d* during the same interval. Area *A* equals area *B*, according to Kepler's Second Law.

that they did so. The statement of this conclusion is known as

> KEPLER'S FIRST LAW: Planets follow elliptical orbits about the sun, which lies at one focus.

He also found that the planets do not move at the same speed at each part of their orbits; they move faster when they are closer to the sun, suggesting that there is something about the sun that *causes* the motion. The connection between the speed of the planet and its position on the orbit is expressed indirectly by

> KEPLER'S SECOND LAW: A line drawn from any planet to the sun sweeps out equal areas in equal times.

Figure 2–4 should help you to understand what the

second law means. Imagine that you can tie a heavily inked elastic thread between the planet *P* and the sun *S*. As the planet moves along the ellipse the thread also moves, leaving an inked-in area behind it. What Kepler's Law predicts is this: If you pick any time interval, the area inked in during the first interval is equal to the area inked in during the next equal interval (although it is a different shape), and that area in turn is equal to the area inked in during a third equal interval, and so on until you have covered the entire ellipse. From this law, and with the help of the figure, you can see that the planet must move faster when it is near the sun than otherwise. During the month when the planet is near the sun it sweeps out area *A* on the diagram; during the month when it is farthest from the sun it sweeps out area *B*. The lines *Sa* and *Sb* are much shorter than the lines *Sc* and *Sd*, so, as the areas are equal, the arc *ab* must be longer that the arc *cd*. Now since the planet takes the same amount of time to go from *a* to *b* as to traverse the shorter distance from *c* to *d*, it has to be moving faster on *ab* than on *cd*. So with Kepler's Second Law died another long-held idea, that the planets always move at a constant speed. In 1609 Kepler published his first two laws in a book called *New Astronomy*.

Kepler's Third Law

Kepler was left with one important question unanswered. Can one express a relation between the period of a planet (the time it takes to go once around the sun, or its year) and the size of this orbit? For ten years he pondered this problem in the intervals between his other works. At last Kepler arrived at the solution which he published in his book *The Harmony of the World* in 1619. This answer formed

KEPLER'S THIRD LAW: The ratio of the squares of the periods of any two planets is equal to the ratio of the cubes of their (average) distance from the sun.

It is easiest to understand Kepler's Third Law with the help of an example. Take Earth and Mars as the two planets we are comparing. The period of Mars is 686.98 days; that of the earth is 365.24 days. The ratio of these two numbers is 1.880 which, when squared, becomes 3.530. The average distance from Mars to the sun is 141,600,000 miles while that of the earth to the sun is 92,900,000 miles. The ratio of these two is 1.524, and the cube of this ratio is 3.538, or not very different from the square of the first ratio. One reason that there is not exact agreement between the two numbers is that Kepler's Law is not exact as he stated it. He did not realize that the masses of the planets and the sun must be taken into account in the calculation. When this is done, his law does indeed become precisely correct; as it stands it is very nearly so.

Kepler's Law points out that the farther a planet is from the sun the longer it will take to go around the sun. The following table bears this out.

PLANETARY PERIODS AND AVERAGE DISTANCES FROM THE SUN

Planet	*Period*	*Average Distance from Sun*
Mercury	87.97 days	36,000,000 miles
Venus	224.70 days	67,200,000 miles
Earth	365.24 days	92,900,000 miles
Mars	686.98 days	141,600,000 miles
Jupiter	11.86 years	483,400,000 miles
Saturn	29.46 years	886,200,000 miles
Uranus	84.01 years	1,782,000,000 miles
Neptune	164.79 years	2,792,400,000 miles
Pluto	248.43 years	3,671,200,000 miles

A Formula for Kepler's Third Law

If we are comparing any two planets (call them A and B) whose periods or years are T_A and T_B and whose average distances from the sun are r_A and r_B, Kepler's Third Law can be written in algebraic form as

$$\frac{T_A^2}{T_B^2} = \frac{r_A^3}{r_B^3}.$$

By cross-multiplying and then dividing first by r_A^3 and then by r_B^3 we get from this:

$$\frac{T_A^2}{r_A^3} = \frac{T_B^2}{r_B^3}.$$

By comparing each planet with each of the others we could arrive at a whole succession of such equations in which each ratio is equal to all the others, so that:

$$\frac{T_A^2}{r_A^3} = \frac{T_B^2}{r_B^3} = \frac{T_C^2}{r_C^3} = \text{and so on.}$$

What this means is that the square of the period of *any* planet divided by the cube of its distance to the sun will always give the same number, no matter which planet you choose. This number is then what we call a *constant,* that is, it does not change from one planet to another; it can be easily calculated and we give it the symbol K. We can write the equation, good for all planets:

$$\frac{T^2}{r^3} = K.$$

Now, with the three laws of Kepler set forth, it was possible for someone to discover the inverse square law of gravity. It is true that almost fifty years elapsed before Isaac Newton did in fact deduce this universal law, but from the year 1619 the way was clear for this discovery. Kepler himself was on the right track with his belief that rays of force radiate from the sun. As the sun turns, thought Kepler, these rays somehow push the planets around with them. The farther the planet is from the sun, the weaker the force of these rays, which explained to Kepler why distant planets moved more slowly than closer ones. We may laugh at this charming notion, but it does show that Kepler had an intuitive feeling that we should look to the sun for the source of motion, an effect that was somehow diminished by distance.

Between Kepler's Laws which governed the motion of the planets and Newton's Law of Gravity which applied to all bodies lay the work of Galileo Galilei.

With Galileo we meet for the first time the concept of gravity, a force. From Galileo's ideas on mechanics, the study of the motion of bodies, Newton found the inspiration for many of his more precisely stated laws of motion.

chapter three FALLING BODIES

Galileo Galilei was a questioner. He had doubted most of what his teachers taught at the University of Pisa; he argued with his associates on the faculty when he himself became a professor there. Galileo was not the sort of person who would believe what Aristotle had taught more than nineteen hundred years before just because everyone else believed these teachings to be self-evident. Certainly not!

Galileo, born in 1584 in the Tuscan city of Pisa, began his contributions to science at an early age. One year after he had left the University of Pisa the young man had invented a hydrostatic balance, and two years later he produced an essay on the center of mass of solid figures, a project which, without the aid of the yet-to-be-invented calculus, was extremely difficult.

As a practical result of this work Galileo was appointed to the chair of mathematics at the University of Pisa, a great honor for a young man of twenty-five years. His tactless and arrogant manner with those who disagreed with his ideas made Galileo very unpopular, and so two years after he joined the faculty he was fired. Galileo bounced into another position, one at the University of Padua, a post he held for nearly twenty years. In Padua his lectures were so well liked that eventually a hall holding two thousand people had to be assigned to him. While he was at Padua, Galileo helped develop the thermometer, the telescope, and the microscope, and he advanced the sciences of hydrostatics and acoustics. The fame brought by Galileo's work and his lectures interfered with his work on his real obsession—the discovery of laws that would describe the way bodies move. He expected that the same laws would apply to bodies moving on earth as to the motion of the stars and the planets. Galileo was, of course, a Copernican. When he heard of the discovery by the Dutch optician's apprentice, Hans Lippershey, that two lenses can be put together to bring distant objects closer, Galileo immediately saw the possibilities of this instrument. He would point it to the skies. The telescope gave Galileo the ammunition he needed to challenge the view that the heavens are perfect, unchangeable, wholly different from the earth, and that the earth is the center about which the heavens move.

Galileo was not disappointed by what he saw. A wrinkly-surfaced moon, a sun marred with spots that came and went, a Venus that went through phases like those of our moon—these were among the observations that were absolutely impossible according to Aristotle, and that made the Copernican theory seem even more plausible. In 1609 Galileo published a booklet, *Message from the Stars,* in which he shared his discoveries with his readers. Needless to say, this pamphlet caused an enormous sensation and angered many, Catholic and Protestant alike. Unfortunately, this was the year in which Galileo left the protection of Padua, which as part of the city-state of Venice was holding out against the forces of the Inquisition.

Persecution by the Inquisition

Because of his fame, and because he was a friend of the duke, Galileo was offered a position as mathematician to the court of the Duke of Tuscany in Florence. This move meant that Galileo could return to his home province of Tuscany—Pisa and Florence are less than fifty miles apart. It also offered Galileo a higher salary and, most important, more free time. Galileo took the position and thus exposed himself to his enemies. Gradually his foes gained ground in Rome, until in 1616 they succeeded in bringing Galileo before the tribunal of the Inquisition. This tribunal commanded Galileo to "abstain altogether from teaching or defending this opinion or doctrine and even from discussing it." Galileo yielded, but did not forget the views he held so firmly. In 1623, when his old friend Cardinal Barberini was elected pope, Galileo began working on *Dialogues on the Great World Systems* and he finished this book six years later. Once again Galileo proclaimed that the earth is not the center of the universe. His vigorous literary style gave the book an enormous audience which could be converted to Galileo's point of view by his convincing arguments. The Church had to act. Once again Galileo went before the tribunal of the Inquisition. He recanted; he was placed under house arrest for the rest of his life;

his *Dialogues* was banned. Galileo had denied the truth, but his spirit was not broken. He wrote his greatest book, *Two New Sciences,* under the double handicap of the need for secrecy and his growing blindness. Galileo's friends managed to smuggle the manuscript to Holland, where it was published in 1638. Four years later Galileo died, totally blind. Later in that year (make of this what you will) Isaac Newton was born.

Falling Bodies

We can find Galileo's discoveries on gravity in *Two New Sciences.* This book is arranged as a conversation between three men, one of whom, Salviati, represents Galileo's point of view. It is Salviati who states those doubts of Galileo which led to a better understanding of gravity. They are here, in Galileo's words:

"Salviati: I greatly doubt that Aristotle ever tested by experiment whether it be true that two stones one weighing ten times as much the other, if allowed to fall, at the same instant, from a height of, say, 100 cubits, would so differ in speed that when the heavier had reached the ground, the other would not have fallen more than 10 cubits."

Galileo's doubts about the motion of falling bodies began when as a young man he noticed some peculiar things about a swinging pendulum. First, he remarked that no matter whether the weight swung in a wide arc or a small one the time it took to go from one side to the other and back (the *period*) remained about the same. When he investigated further, Galileo found that as long as the length of the cord remained the same it did not matter how heavy the weight was. The period of the pendulum *was independent* of the weight of the bob. Since the motion of a pendulum is a lot like that of a body falling freely except that the end of a pendulum is held into an arc, Galileo felt very strongly that weight would not affect the speed of any falling body.

Here we find a remarkable difference between Galileo and the natural philosophers who came before him. Galileo knew that it was not enough to "feel"; he had to prove his intuition by performing an experiment. Before Galileo the "truth" was usually reached by pure thought unaided and unchecked by observation. While it was surprising that Kepler altered his theory to fit Brahe's observations, it was even more unheard-of to actually set up an experiment to verify a theory. For this reason Galileo is sometimes called the first modern scientist.

The Experiment

The legend which often provides illustrations for physics books holds that Galileo went about proving his theory by climbing to the top of the Leaning Tower of Pisa, Figure 3–1, and dropping from it two balls of the same size but of greatly different weights. The watching crowd, says the story, saw

Figure 3–1. The Leaning Tower at Pisa. Galileo may have demonstrated his theory of falling bodies by dropping balls simultaneously from the top of this tower. He proved his theory by making measurements with inclined planes.

the two balls hit the ground at the same time and, struck with awe, believed. In fact, Galileo was much more accurate than that. If he did perform the Leaning Tower experiment at all, it was not meant to be an exact proof of his theories but only a dramatic demonstration of them. For his own satisfaction Galileo needed much greater precision.

Arguing that a body that falls from a certain height h has the same speed when it hits the ground as it would have had it rolled down an inclined plane of any slope *but* with the same height *h,* Galileo set to work making measurements with inclined planes. His planes were pieces of molding with grooves cut into them. We shall let Galileo, through the mouth of Salviati, describe his experiment.

"Having made this groove very straight, smooth and polished, and having lined it with parchment, also as smooth and polished as possible, we rolled along it a hard, smooth and round bronze ball. Having placed this board in a sloping position . . . we rolled the ball . . . noting the time required to make the descent. We repeated this experiment more than once in order to measure the time with an accuracy such that the deviation between two observations never exceeded one tenth of a pulsebeat." (See Figure 3–2.)

Figure 3–2. Galileo's experiment. Ball is rolled down inclined grooved plane, and the descent is timed.

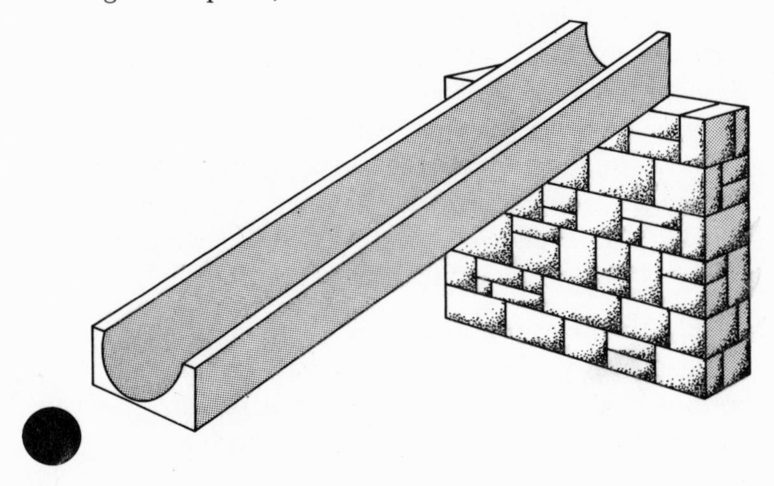

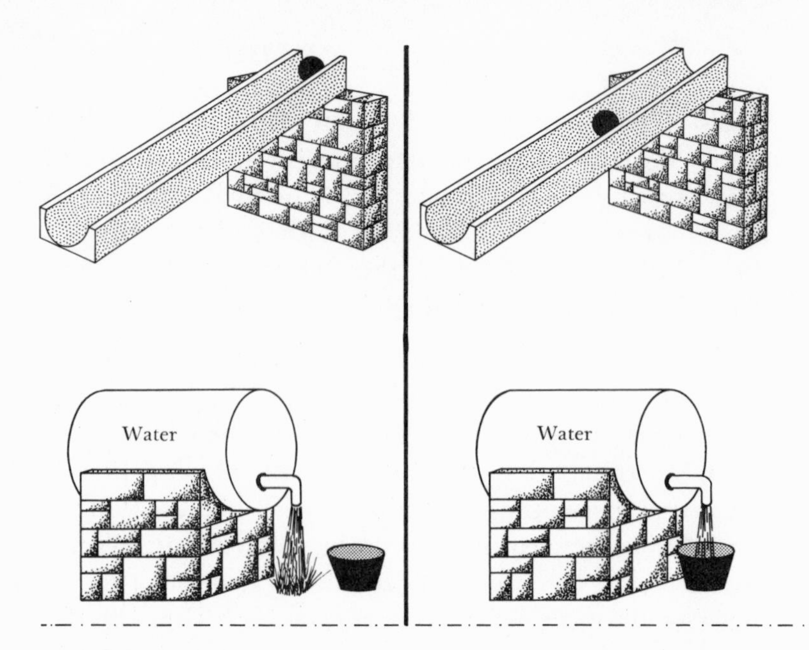

A sloppy experiment was not good enough for Galileo! Notice how he emphasizes the polishing, the smoothness that he needed to reduce friction so that its effects could be neglected. As you can imagine, the accurate measurement of time posed a problem for Galileo; a precise timepiece simply did not exist. Galileo was forced to use a "water clock," an ingenious method which replaced the clock by the one accurate instrument available—the balance. One might say that Galileo "weighed" time. We shall let him explain how this extraordinary feat was accomplished.

"For the measurement of time, we employed a large vessel of water placed in an elevated position; to the bottom of this vessel was soldered a pipe of small diameter giving a thin jet of water, which we collected

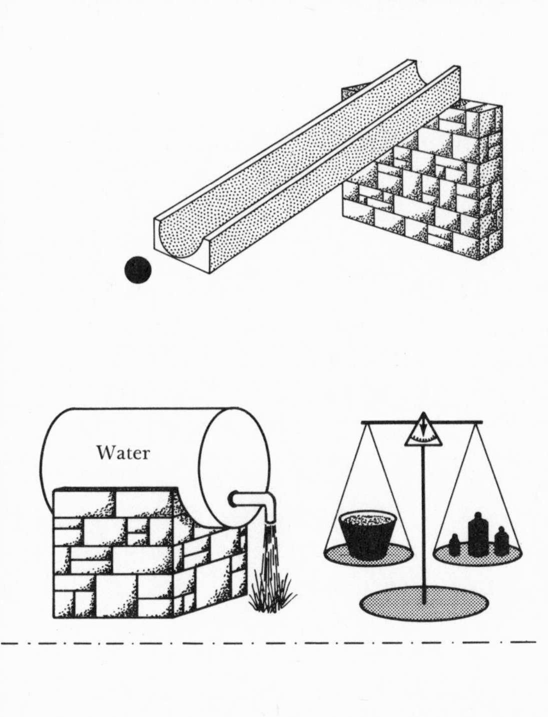

Figure 3–3. "Weighing" time intervals. Before the ball begins its descent the glass beaker is empty. As the ball is released the beaker is placed under the jet of water. As soon as the ball reaches the bottom of the inclined plane the beaker is removed and weighed. As the flow of water is constant the amount of water in the beaker is proportional to the elapsed time.

in a small glass during the time of each descent, whether for the whole length of the channel or for a part of its length; the water thus collected was weighed, after each descent, on a very accurate balance; the differences and ratios of these weights gave us the differences and ratios of the times, and this with such accuracy that although the operation was repeated many, many times, there was no appreciable discrepancy in the results."

A reservoir of water from which flowed a constant stream of water, a container placed under the stream only while the ball was descending—such was Galileo's "clock." See Figure 3–3. There remained the problem of making the connection between grams of water and seconds of time. Granted that the more water there was in the container, the more time had passed, Galileo still had to convert weight to time. He got around this dilemma by working with ratios. The various amounts of water collected in the containers during the various descents were *proportional* to the time needed to make these descents. By comparing the weight of water collected during one descent with that collected during another, Galileo was able to rid himself of the bothersome units of weight and time and come up with a result expressed only in ratios. He could say, for example, that the time needed for the ball to roll down the first quarter of the channel was one half the time needed to make the entire descent.

An Equation for Falling Bodies

What did Galileo learn from these carefully performed experiments? First, he was able to establish a mathematical relationship between the *distance* traveled by the ball and the *time* needed to move this distance. Here is the equation:

$$\frac{\text{first distance}}{\text{second distance}} = \frac{(\text{first time})^2}{(\text{second time})^2}$$

or

$$\frac{d_1}{d_2} = \frac{t_1^2}{t_2^2}.$$

What this means is that if the ball rolled down 8 feet

of channel in ½ second then it would need one second to roll down 32 feet of the same channel.

Now, at long last, the motion of falling bodies could be described by an equation. This formula did not tell the whole story of gravity—far from it—but, as a physicist will not take seriously any concept that cannot be expressed by an equation, it can be said that Galileo's experiments gave birth to the idea of gravity.

A very important fact that emerged from Galileo's experiments was that the weight of the balls did not, after all, affect the speed at which they fell. Galileo's intuition was right—*heavy balls do not fall faster than light balls.* Many of Galileo's contemporaries could not accept this result even when they saw the demonstration with their own eyes. The world was not yet ready for a science based on experiment.

Now you might ask, and Galileo did ask, what sort of situation would produce an equation like the previous one? If you examine this formula, you can see that it can be rewritten for one descent only:

Distance fallen is proportional to the square of the time of falling,

or

$$d = kt^2.$$

We arrive at this equation following the same reasoning that we used to go from the first equation for Kepler's Third Law to the form on page 39. With the equation in this form we can more easily see its significance.

An Important Difference

You notice that the equation $d = kt^2$ which expresses the relationship between distance and time for a falling body is quite different from the old familiar formula:

Distance equals rate times time

or

$$d = vt.$$

This equation, which you used in grade school, was true only for a body moving at a *constant* rate of speed v, although doubtless no one pointed this out to you at the time. There is a big difference between the two equations: in one case distance is proportional to time; in the other case, distance is proportional to the *square* of the time.

Acceleration

Galileo realized that because falling bodies could be described by an equation of the form $d = kt^2$ they must be constantly accelerated. Before he could come to this conclusion Galileo had to have a clear idea of this concept of acceleration; in fact he was the first person to understand its importance to the study of moving bodies. Galileo's ideas on acceleration started from his realization that a body, once set in motion, will continue to move unless some force stops it, or to put this another way, *a force is not needed to keep* *a body moving at a constant speed.** Now this was quite the opposite of what Aristotle had taught—the common-sense idea that a force *is* needed to keep a body in motion. The fact that Aristotle was wrong and Galileo right was made clear by Newton. He stated this principle explicitly in his First Law of Motion.

If a force is not needed to prolong motion, what *does* a force do? It produces acceleration! Again, Galileo recognized this fact which Newton later stated in mathematical form as his Second Law of Motion. A force applied to a body gives that body an acceleration which is proportional to its mass. What then, exactly, is acceleration? Acceleration is the rate at which velocity changes. Velocity is what we call a *vector,* that is, it is a quantity that not only has a value associated with it, but also a direction. You can say that the speed of a car is fifty miles per hour, but if you wish to give its velocity you must say, for example, that it is going north at fifty miles per hour. Acceleration may be the rate of change of *speed* of the body, but it may also be the rate of change of *direction,* so that even if the body is maintaining a constant speed it can be accelerated. Figure 3–4 shows the three ways in which a car can be accelerated.

The acceleration may be constant or not. A car moving in traffic usually experiences nonuniform acceleration. It may move at 10 miles per hour for five minutes,

* Why then can't we achieve perpetual motion? Because in the real world friction forces are present to slow down everything that moves. Motion will continue without a force much longer in a vacuum where air resistance is practically zero. The better the vacuum the longer will the motion persist.

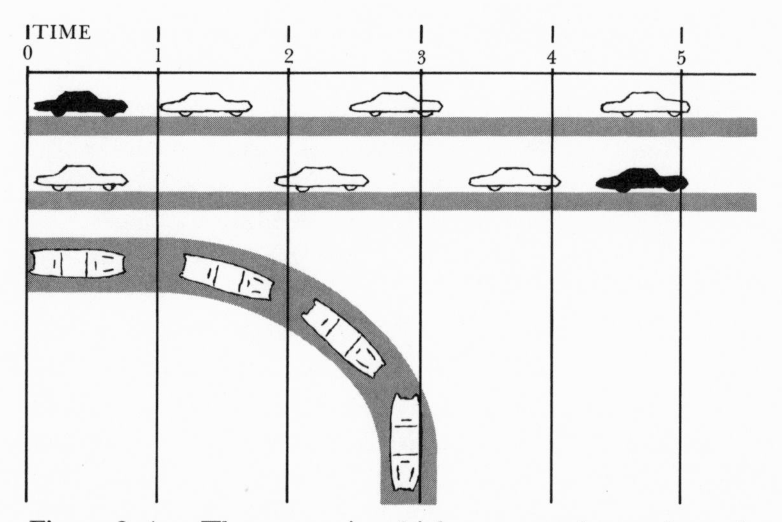

Figure 3–4. Three ways in which a car can be accelerated. In the top picture the car covers more and more distance with each interval of time. In the middle picture the car travels less distance during an interval as time goes on. In the third picture the car covers the same distance in each interval but its direction changes.

get up to 25 mph for another ten minutes and then reach a highway and go off at 60 mph. *Its* acceleration is not constant. To calculate the distance this car went would be more difficult than if it were being uniformly accelerated, as it is, for example, when it starts. At the start its speed is 0; one second later its speed is 10 mph; two seconds later it is 20 mph; three seconds later it is 30 mph. As you can see, this acceleration *is* uniform; it is 10 mph per second. Whenever the acceleration of a body is uniform we can find it easily—

we subtract the speed at the start from the final speed and divide by the time during which the body is moving: $a = \frac{v_{\text{final}} - v_{\text{initial}}}{t}$.

Accelerated Motion

Now that we can define acceleration we are in a better position to return to Galileo's next calculations. The question he had to answer was this: How far does a uniformly accelerated body move in a certain known amount of time? We cannot use $d = vt$ in this case, because as the body is accelerated the speed is, by our definition, not constant. What then *can* one do to calculate the distance? Galileo showed that the way out of this dilemma is to *modify* $d = vt$. As long as the acceleration is constant you can replace the speed v by the average speed throughout the period of motion. You can find this average speed very easily by simply subtracting the initial speed from the final speed and dividing by two, and since the initial speed is zero in the problems that interest us in this book, the average speed is equal to the final speed divided by two. This gives a formula for distance traveled by a body moving with constant acceleration from a standing start to a final speed of v: $d = vt/2$. Now since the initial speed is zero, we find from the equation for acceleration just given in the last section that $a = v/t$ or $v = at$. If we put this value for v into the equation above for d, we find that $d = (at)(t/2)$, or

$$d = \frac{at^2}{2} \quad \text{(for constant acceleration).}$$

Now the really interesting thing about this equation is that it has the same *form* as that of the equation on page 51 which gives the distance fallen in a certain time t. In both cases this distance is proportional to the *square* of the time. (The letter a in the equation above stands for acceleration, which is, remember, constant; this is why we say that d is proportional to t^2.) Galileo concluded that falling takes place with constant acceleration. As a falling body goes faster and faster, the change in speed during each time interval is always the same.

The Acceleration of Gravity

We call the special kind of acceleration that a falling body undergoes the *acceleration of gravity* and label it g. The equation for falling bodies on page 51 is then more properly rewritten

$$d = \frac{gt^2}{2}.$$

The value of g can be found by various methods which we discuss in chapter 6; the values are as follows:

$$g = 32 \text{ feet per second per second}$$

or

$$g = 9.8 \text{ meters per second per second}$$

or

$$g = 980 \text{ centimeters per second per second.}$$

A New Kind of Force

As we saw a few pages back, the fact that a body is accelerated implies that it is acted upon by a *force.* When mechanical forces are involved you can often see the force acting: you can see a ball being hit by a bat, or a bulldozer pushing earth out of the way. In the same way, when Galileo realized that the falling balls were accelerated, he knew that they were being acted upon by a force, no less real because he could not see what produced it. This unseen force which causes bodies to be accelerated toward the center of the earth we call *gravity.*

Mass and Weight

So far we have been using the terms "mass" and "weight" without defining them. We have reached a point now where we can show the relationship between the two. The mass of a body is a measure of the amount of matter it contains; its weight, on the other hand, is the force exerted by the earth on this mass. The weight w of a body on earth is defined in terms of its mass m:

$$w = mg.$$

The force (weight) is equal to the mass times the acceleration, a fact that we have already mentioned briefly in passing, and shall meet again in the next chapter.

chapter four

UNIVERSAL GRAVITATION

The theory of universal gravitation did not suddenly and completely take form in Isaac Newton's brain right after the famous apple fell. Alas, nothing is that simple, even for a genius. The falling apple *triggered* a set of circumstances which were superbly favorable for producing new ideas. Before he had received his degree from Cambridge University in 1665 Newton had worked out the well-known binomial theorem. At the end of that year, his head full of the learning of the past, self-confident from his own accomplishments, Newton was suddenly blessed with solitude and oceans of time. The apple flashing by reminded Newton of the question that was very much in the minds of the thinkers of that time: Is gravity solely an earthly phenomenon? The effects of gravity were felt as high as man had climbed; could it be possible that it went beyond the earth? Was the moon subject to this law? Could it be, wondered Newton, that it was the earth's gravity that held the moon in its orbit? And what made the planets move in elliptical paths? Newton realized that, once set in motion, a planet would continue to move in a straight line. But to move in a curved path the planet must be acted upon by some force. What was the force? Could it be gravitation? And was it a force felt throughout the universe? These were some of the questions that came to the young man during a long enforced stay in the country.

Woolsthorpe

Newton's holiday came about because of the Great Plague, which in the short time from July to September of 1665 had already killed more than one tenth of the population of London. For fear of the plague Cambridge University was closed in the fall, and Newton went back to his ancestral home in Woolsthorpe, where he had been born on Christmas Day, 1642. One might imagine that far from the stimulation of the university Newton's scientific work would end. This was absolutely not the case! In fact, the period Newton spent at Woolsthorpe was perhaps the most productive eighteen months the world of science has ever known. By November, Newton had already worked out the elements of differential calculus. By the next January Newton understood the action of a prism on white light, by May he was beginning to develop integral calculus. And in the same year, 1666, the idea came to him that has always been linked with his name —the concept of universal gravitation. All these works were more than important; Newton was creating new ways of thinking.

When he returned to Cambridge early in 1667, it was as a member of the faculty. Now Newton began to show his characteristic secrecy about his work. He was very reluctant to publish anything, and did so only to establish his priority. The only exception to this behavior had to do with his construction of a reflecting telescope. This instrument used a mirror instead of a lens for magnification, and so was free of the disturbing colored fringes you often see on the edge of a telescope image. In a paper describing this telescope, Newton included a summary of his experiments with prisms and his conclusion that white light is composed of light of many colors. Because he could not abide criticism, Newton was infuriated by the skeptical reaction of scientists to his theory of color. This experience reinforced his determination never to share his results with his fellow scientists.

All through his life Newton carried on vulgar squabbles with many of the scientific figures of his day. He quarreled mainly with Robert Hooke over the question of credit for the idea of the inverse-square law of gravitation and over work on the optical effects of thin films. Newton's disputes with the German Leibnitz are notorious; Leibnitz had independently invented calculus and both men claimed priority.

The Principia and Opticks

Despite his thorny personality Newton was known as a man whose ideas were worth attention. The astronomer Edmund Halley, who predicted the appearance of Halley's Comet, gained Newton's confidence and finally did the next to impossible: he persuaded Newton to publish a complete summary of his theories of mechanics. This book, the *Principia,* begins with the statement of what are now known as Newton's Laws of Motion and then goes on to apply them to various simple situations. The book is a real treasure trove, treating of hydrodynamics, wave motion, the origin of the equatorial bulge, the precession of the equinoxes—and much, much more. The part of the book that interests us here is his derivation of the inverse-square law of gravitation from Kepler's Laws; we shall soon see how this was done.

After the publication of the *Principia* in 1687, Newton's position in the world was completely changed. Instead of criticism, his works now met acclaim. In 1705 he was knighted and became Sir Isaac Newton. As a member of Parliament, as Master of the Mint, Newton had little time for further scientific work. The great mind was also diverted by curious pastimes—alchemy, Biblical chronology, and writing of carefully hidden anti-Trinitarian tracts. Nevertheless, in 1703, when Hooke was safely buried, Newton ventured to publish another book, one that Hooke would surely have torn to shreds. This work, *Opticks,* is an account of experiments that Newton performed on lenses and prisms, telescopes, thin films, the nature of color, refraction, and diffraction along with an interpretation of these experiments. The *Opticks* shows Newton to be as great an experimental physicist as the *Principia* shows him to be a great mathematician. It is hard to believe that one man could be capable of writing two such different masterpieces.

Newton's last years were passed in ease and honor and good health. He was eighty before he suffered a real illness, a bladder stone. Five years later an acute bladder attack took his life on March 20, 1727.

Newton was not the only student of gravity; in the coffeehouses where intellectuals gathered for conversation the notion of a gravity that extended throughout the universe was bandied about until it was impossible to give credit to one person instead of another for an idea that was so common. The real problem was to determine the mathematical form of this force, and to show that the same force acted at a large distance from the earth.

Newton's secrecy makes it very hard for us to know just how he went about solving his problems—which clues he followed up first, what steps he used in arriving at his conclusions. He preferred us to see the results all tidied up and set out in orderly fashion as in his book the *Principia.* He spared us the nasty but interesting details; we must try to reconstruct them.

Newton's Laws of Motion

In an amazing tour de force Newton himself forged the tools that he would need to work out his results. His own fantastic work, and all of classical mechanics, follow logically from the laws of motion that he stated.

We shall simply write down the laws themselves without giving the background of thought that led Newton to state them as correct. We have already mentioned the first two laws several times.

NEWTON'S FIRST LAW OF MOTION: A body, once set in motion, will continue to move *in a straight line* unless acted upon by a force.

NEWTON'S SECOND LAW OF MOTION: The force required to produce a certain acceleration in a body is equal to the mass of this body times that acceleration. This is written mathematically in the fundamental equation:

$$F = ma.$$

NEWTON'S THIRD LAW OF MOTION: When one body exerts a force upon a second body, that second body exerts in return a force upon the first body. The forces are equal in amount and opposite in direction to each other. The second force is called a *reaction force.*

Centripetal Force

Newton's aim was to find out about the force that was needed to keep the planets moving in curved paths instead of straight lines. We call such a force which attracts bodies to a center *centripetal,* which means "center-seeking." You can find out a bit about centripetal force by performing a simple experiment. If you dare, swing a pail half full of water *very* quickly over your head. The water stays in the pail, even when the pail is upside-down! Why? What you *really* should ask, if you think about this situation, is not, "Why does the water stay in the pail?" but, "Why does the water

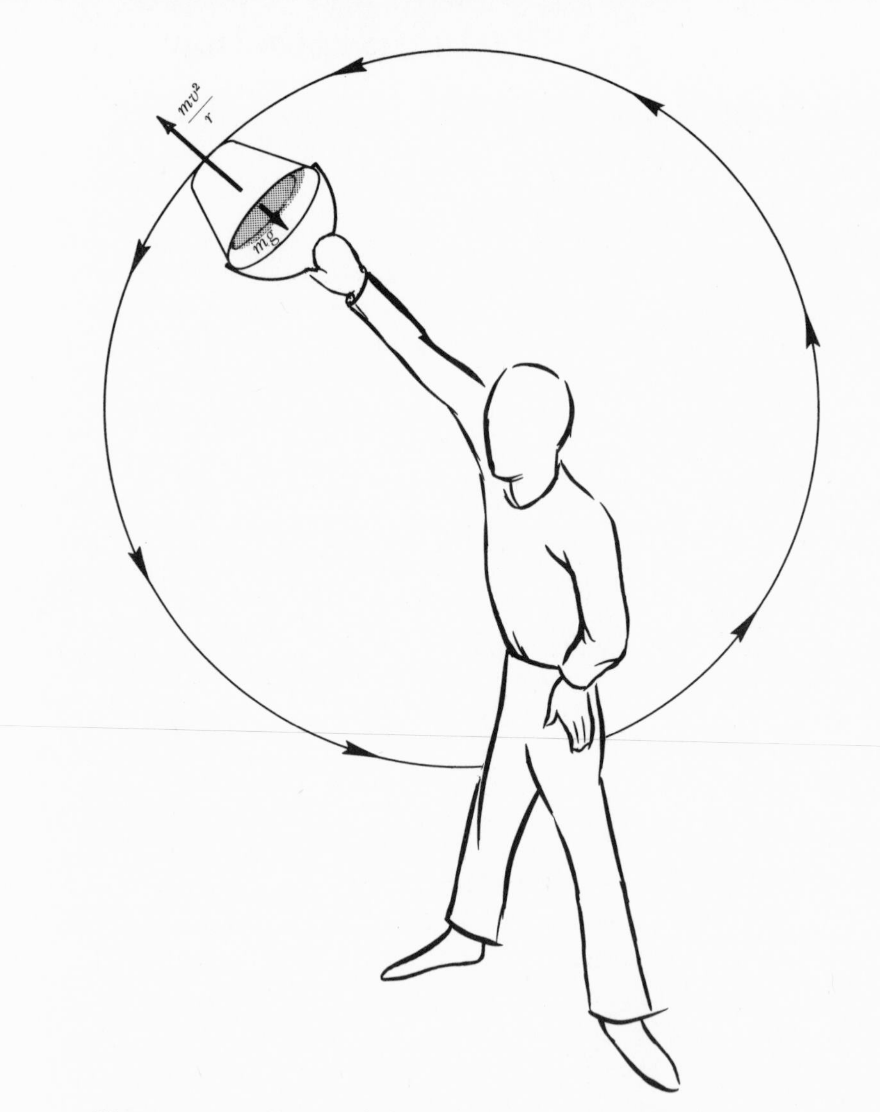

Figure 4–1. Forces acting on water in a pail. As the pail is swung up it must be held in with a centripetal force mv^2/r. When the pail is overhead the weight of the water mg must be balanced by the centrifugal reaction force mv^2/r or the water will fall out of the bucket.

ever fall out of the pail?" What happens is this: As you swing the pail up you set the water in motion too. See Figure 4–1. The water would keep on moving forever, obeying Newton's First Law, except for two forces that act upon it. One of these is gravity which tends to pour the water out onto you. There is another force acting on the water—that exerted by the bottom of the pail which holds the water in. This inward force is provided by your arm; the faster you swing the bucket the more the water tries to get away and the harder you must pull. To put this another way, the faster you turn the bucket the more centripetal force you must apply to keep it from flying off. If, on the other hand, you do not swing the pail very fast, the water has such a small tendency to keep moving out that when the bucket is above your head the water is not moving upward fast enough to balance the effect of gravity, and you get wet. (You *did* get wet? Oh, well, you were getting sick of that sweater anyway, weren't you?)

"Centrifugal" Force

Now we come to a curious misnaming which can still be found in some textbooks. From what we were saying above it may seem as though the swinging of the pail produced a sort of outward force which you felt as a pull on your arm. This imaginary force has been given a name, *centrifugal force* (center-fleeing force). You will often see these words in books and periodicals. But, no matter how much your arm may hurt from the pull on it, it is important to realize that centrifugal forces are only reaction forces, reactions to the centripetal forces which are needed to hold moving bodies into curved paths. The pictures below may help you understand *why* an inward force is needed to keep a body moving along a curve instead of a straight line.

One way of thinking of a circle is to imagine it as

Figure 4–2. A circle can be thought of as an infinite number of straight lines each at right angles to an infinite number of radii. Here we have only 36 radii and yet the resulting figure is very nearly a circle.

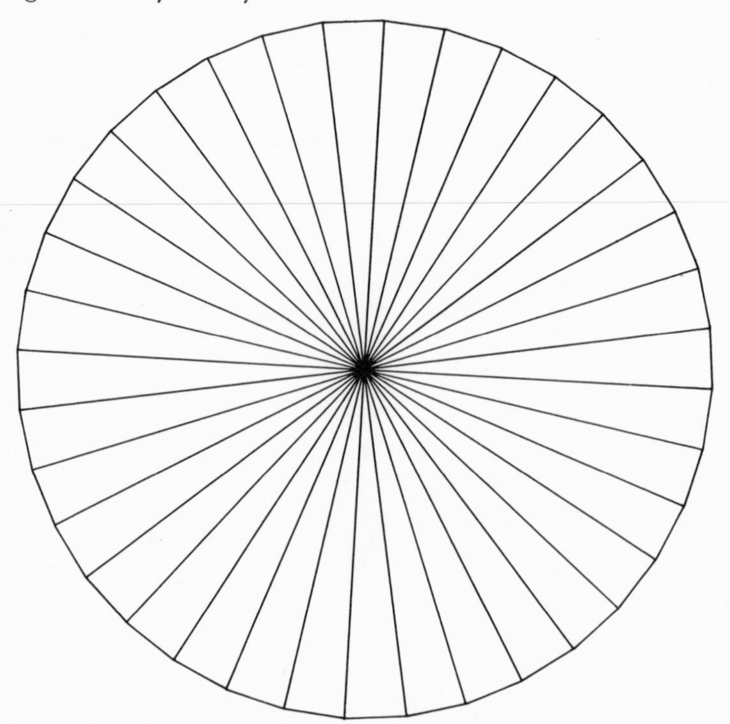

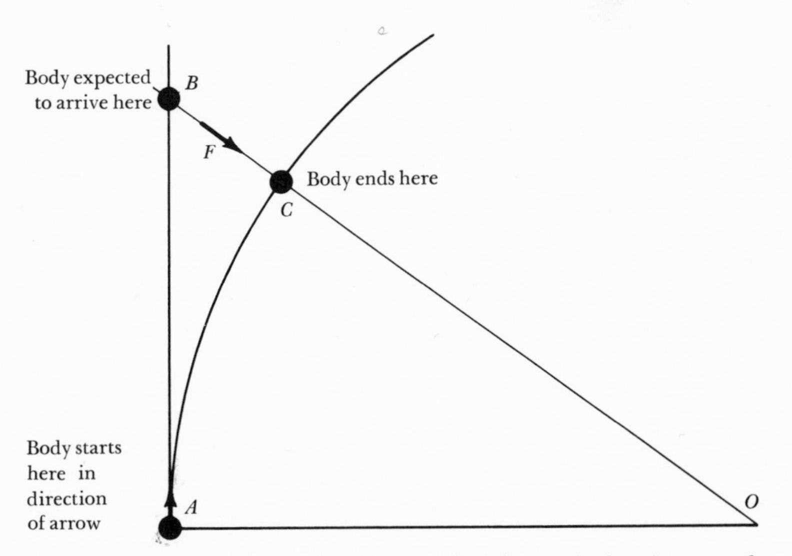

Figure 4–3. Motion of body moving in a circle. A central force F must act on the body to deflect it from B to C.

made up of an infinite number of straight lines, each at right angles to an infinite number of radii, as in Figure 4–2. The next sketch, Figure 4–3, shows a part of this circle expanded and exaggerated. If a body is started moving at point A (no matter how), it would ordinarily, if no force acts on it, continue to move in a straight line so that at some later time you would find the body at point B. If, instead, you find the body at point C because it is moving in a circle around O, you conclude that a force must be acting on it to move it in toward the center, O. This inward, or centripetal, force acts directly from the center and its value is

$$F_{\text{centripetal}} = \frac{mv^2}{r}.$$

In this equation r stands for the radius of the curve, m for the mass of the body, and v for its speed. You can easily see that the faster the body moves, the more force must be used to hold it in. This is the formula for centripetal force, but as they are equal and opposite you will see this expression given for centrifugal force also. You can surely think of many examples of "centrifugal force"—the behavior of a car going around a turn, the motion of a small light object placed on a turning phonograph record. In these cases it looks as though the circular motion produces a force that makes the bodies fly off. In fact, just the opposite is the case. Just because they are moving, the bodies have a tendency to move in a straight line; they only fly off if there is no force applied to keep them in.

From Kepler's Law to the Inverse Square Law of Gravity

Now let us see how we can use what we have learned about centripetal force as we return to the question of gravity. We are about to see how Kepler's Third Law can be combined with the equation for centripetal force to lead to an equation for gravity. Instead of following Newton exactly, we shall introduce some simplifications to make our work easier. Our method will be the same as Newton's, however, and we shall arrive at the same results as well as an appreciation of his work.

The simplification that we make is to assume that the orbits of the planets are circles instead of ellipses.

This is not so far from the truth; first of all a circle is, as you saw, a special kind of ellipse. In the case of the planet orbits the ellipses *are* nearly circular. What we gain by assuming a circular orbit is a *constant* speed for the planet, whereas as the planet moves about an elliptical path its speed changes, as Kepler pointed out. A constant speed for the planet makes the arithmetic much simpler because we can use the formula "rate times time equals distance" in our calculations. The "distance" we use in this equation is the circumference of the orbit, or $2\pi r$ where r is the radius of the orbit. The "time" is that time needed to make one revolution about the sun, or the period T. The equation then becomes:

$$2\pi r = vT.$$

By solving this for T we get:

$$T = \frac{2\pi r}{v}.$$

If we now put this value for T into the equation that expresses Kepler's Third Law ($T^2/r^3 = K$; page 39), we find:

$$\frac{4\pi^2}{v^2 r} = K$$

and solving this for v^2 we get:

$$v^2 = \frac{4\pi^2}{rK}.$$

Now the centripetal force (we do not need to call it gravity yet) that holds the planets in their orbits is, from the last section, equal to mv^2/r where m is the planet mass, v its orbital speed, and r the radius. The speed of the planet is given above, and if we put this value into the equation for centripetal force we get:

$$F_{\text{centripetal}} = \frac{m\ (4\pi^2)}{r^2\ (K)}.$$

The numbers inside the parentheses are all constant, so this equation tells us that the centripetal force exerted on the planet is proportional to its mass and *inversely* proportional to the *square* of the radius of the orbit. The larger the radius (the farther the planet from the sun), the *smaller* the force on the planet. Because the radius appears squared in the denominator the force gets smaller very quickly with increased distance from the sun. If the distance is doubled, the force goes down to one quarter what it was, as seen in Figure 4–4; if you treble the distance, the force becomes one ninth as great; if you pick a distance four times as great, you find a force only one sixteenth the original value. This kind of force is called an inverse square force.

Gravity and the Moon

Now that we have seen that the sun attracts the planets with an inverse square force, we are tempted to wonder if our own earth's gravity is not the same sort of force. The problem for Newton was to get far enough away from the earth to find out whether or not gravity gets weaker with distance. The highest mountains he could climb were not high enough to show a difference that Newton could measure; in any case he was not much of a mountain climber. But there was the moon! If the earth's gravity reached to the moon, Newton would use the moon itself as part of his laboratory to measure the earth's gravity.

Newton proceeded by simple and straightforward steps. He was able to calculate the centripetal force holding the moon in its orbit, and therefore its centripetal acceleration. Next he worked out the value one would expect to find for the acceleration of gravity at the distance of the moon's orbit *if the earth's gravity were an inverse square force.* Newton found that the two values for acceleration were the same! He could conclude from this result that, first, it *is* the earth's gravity that provides the centripetal force that leashes in the moon, and, second, the earth's gravity *is* an inverse square force. The calculations are simple; let us now see how they are performed.

Figure 4–4. The effect of distance on the gravitational force between two bodies.

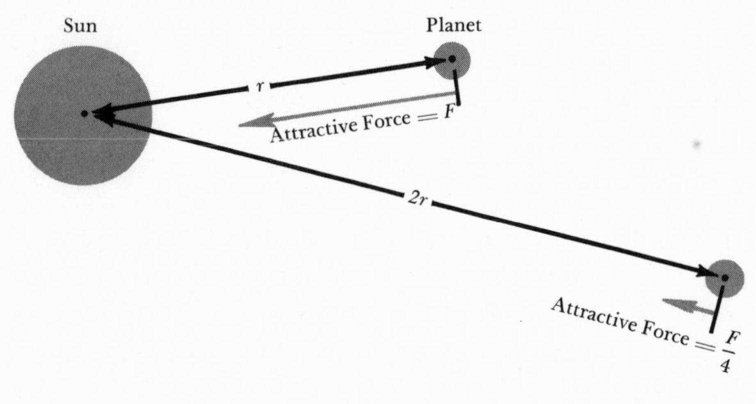

Centripetal Acceleration of the Moon

The centripetal force felt by the moon is:

$$F_c = \frac{mv^2}{r}$$

where m is the moon's mass, r the radius of its orbit, and v its speed around the orbit. According to Newton's Second Law this force must produce an acceleration toward the earth, and the value of this acceleration is, since $F = ma$:

$$a_c = \frac{v^2}{r}.$$

We can calculate this value very easily. We find v as we did earlier, using the approximation that the orbit is circular. As before, $v = 2\pi r/T$ where T is the moon's period, 27.3 days, which was known at Newton's time, as was r. If we put this value for v into the equation above for a_c, we find:

$$a_c = \frac{4\pi^2 r}{T^2}.$$

We substitute the values $r = 384{,}000{,}000$ or 3.84×10^8 meters, and $T = 27.3$ days or 2.35×10^6 seconds, to get a value of $a_c = .0027$ meters per second per second. This is the acceleration with which the moon is falling toward the earth, a fall that never ends in a crash, however, because the moon is also trying to fly off at a tangent to its orbit. You can imagine this situation by looking at Figure 4–3. The body which starts at A and ends at C is the moon; the earth is at O. The distance BC can be thought of as the distance the moon has fallen from its tangent path.

The Acceleration of Gravity at the Moon's Orbit

We know what the acceleration of gravity is at a distance of 4,000 miles from the center of the earth; this is the earth's surface, and the experiments of Galileo showed that it is 9.8 meters per second per second. Now, if our earth's gravity is indeed an inverse square force, how much acceleration does it produce at a distance of 384,000,000 meters from the earth's center, where the moon is? If we compare the forces acting on the same mass m at two different distances from the source, we find for the ratio of these forces:

$$\frac{F_1}{F_2} = \frac{r_2^2}{r_1^2}.$$

Since $F = ma$, the ratio of the accelerations produced by these forces is the same (the masses cancel):

$$\frac{a_1}{a_2} = \frac{r_2^2}{r_1^2}.$$

We can use this equation to compare the acceleration of gravity at the surface of the earth with that at the moon's orbit. The radius of the earth, or the distance from the center to the surface, is 4,000 miles or 6.38×10^6 meters. If a_1 is the acceleration of gravity at the moon's orbit, and if we put the numbers above into the previous equation, we find:

$$a_1 = a_2 \left[\frac{r_2^2}{r_1^2}\right] = 9.8 \left[\frac{6.38 \times 10^6}{3.84 \times 10^8}\right]^2$$

$$= .0027 \text{ meters per second per second.}$$

Since the acceleration of gravity at the moon's orbit shows such a remarkable agreement with the accelera-tion that is needed to hold the moon in this orbit, it is more than reasonable to assume that the *two are really one and the same.*

Universal Gravitation?

Since the same sort of attractive force holds the planets to the sun and the moon to the earth, we cannot be blamed for wondering if the same force acts everywhere in the universe. We have no proof that it does, but there are strong hints that it exists. Newton thought so too; he used the following argument to ar-rive at a law of universal gravitation. The reasoning is fairly subtle, and if you like you can skip it and go on to the conclusion; on the other hand, you might find it fun to follow the steps.

When the sun exerts a force F_g on a planet, then, by Newton's Third Law, that planet exerts the same amount of force on the sun. What does this mean, or matter? The force F_g is proportional to the planet's mass m as you can see from the equation on page 67. (But you notice that we have given $F_{\text{centripetal}}$ the new and simpler label of F_g where g stands for gravity.) At the same time the reaction force F_r exerted by the planet on the sun is proportional to the mass of the *sun* M, since $F_r = Ma$. And both forces are equal! This must mean that *each* force is proportional both to the mass of the planet and to the mass of the sun. With this knowledge we can rewrite the equation on page 67 as:

$$F_g = \frac{GmM}{r^2}.$$

This equation gathers together the information that we have about the force of attraction between planet and sun, and admits our ignorance of just exactly *what* is the value of the proportionality constant. We call it G, the *gravitational constant.*

It was Newton's belief that G would turn out to be a universal constant, that the equation above would prove to apply between any two bodies in the universe. For this reason he stated his law of universal gravitation:

$$F = \frac{m_1 m_2 G}{r^2}$$

in which m_1 is the mass of the first body, m_2 the mass of the second body, and r the distance between their centers.

Since the time when this law was first stated scientists have used it, always maintaining a watch for some occasion when the law might be broken. So far it has not been broken.

chapter five

GRAVITY AND THE SOLAR SYSTEM

After reading the last chapter you know that the force of gravity does not belong to the earth alone. It is an attractive force between bodies of any mass, big or small. The closer these bodies are, the larger the force. You have not told the whole story when you say that an apple is attracted to the earth—the earth is also attracted *to the apple.* The force of attraction is much less successful in moving the heavy earth than in moving the light apple, which is the reason that the apple's gravity is barely noticeable. As you might imagine, the gravitational constant G is very small indeed. It is surprising to learn that as early as 1797 a dabbler in science, Henry Lord Cavendish, was able to measure this small quantity.

The Cavendish Experiment

On the right, Figure 5–1, is a sketch of an apparatus similar to Lord Cavendish's. Two small spheres, each of mass m, are joined by a light rod. The rod is suspended by a gossamer thread; during the experiment, the turning of the rod is barely detectable. This motion must be magnified; this is done by mounting an illuminated mirror, as you can see in the picture. The mirror reflects its light on a distant screen, and the slightest change in its position shows up as a much greater change in the position of the reflected light. This whole ensemble is placed inside a glass box which acts as a shield against currents of air. Large spheres

Figure 5–1. The Cavendish experiment. The light rod and the masses *m* move from the first position to a new position in the direction shown when the masses *M* are brought up to the glass box.

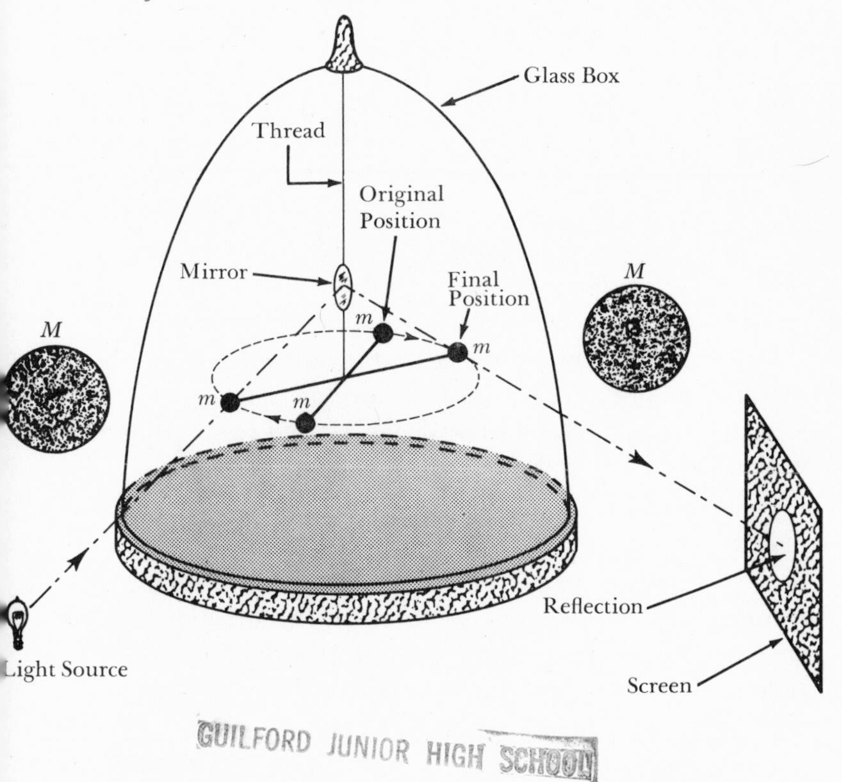

of mass M are suspended outside the box so that they can be turned to various positions around the axis of the inner assembly.

To perform the experiment, the system is first allowed to quiet down; when nothing is moving, the outer balls are moved through a known angle to a new position around the inner axis. The small balls, because of the mutual attraction, move toward the big balls, and as they do this the rod twists an incredibly small amount. (It is because of this turning of the rod, and therefore its thread suspension, that the small spheres cannot move all the way to end up next to the large spheres. The thread has a resistance to twisting.) As the rod twists, the light reflected from the mirror moves a very small but measurable amount. From this measurement and knowing how much force was needed to produce a certain amount of twist in the string, Cavendish was able to calculate the force of attraction between the spheres. From the value of this force, as well as the masses of the spheres, Cavendish was able to use Newton's equation of universal gravitation (page 75) to calculate the value of G, the gravitational constant. How splendid it is that from a specific experiment one can obtain a number as general, as good throughout the universe, as G, the gravitational constant! Surely this is one of the great beauties of physics!

The value that Cavendish arrived at for G was 6.75×10^{-8} in the system of units that uses centimeters, grams, and seconds (cgs). Compare this with the modern value of 6.67×10^{-8} cgs. Not bad work for an amateur! In this book we generally use the meter-kilogram-second (mks) system, and $G = 6.67 \times 10^{-11}$ mks.

How Great Are Gravitational Forces?

The small value of G as a multiplier shows that the forces of attraction between even quite heavy objects are minute. What, for example, is the (gravitational) attraction between you and a friend? For this experiment you must stand 100 meters apart. (If you are closer than that the calculation becomes very difficult.) When two bodies are far enough apart we can consider that they behave as spheres whose weight is concentrated at their centers. We assume that one of you weighs 121 pounds (55 kilograms) and that the other weighs 165 pounds (75 kilograms). These values and that of G go into Newton's equation on page 75, and we get:

$$F = \frac{m_1 m_2\, G}{r^2} = \frac{(55)(75)(6.67 \times 10^{-11})}{100^2}$$

$$F = 2.75 \times 10^{-11} \text{ kilograms.}$$

The attractive force is only .00000000006 pounds between you and your friend. Nevertheless it *is* gravity and not love that makes the world go round.

Weighing the Earth

It may seem unbelievable, but at this point you have enough information to weigh the earth.

You can do this by combining Newton's Second Law and his law of universal gravitation. We begin by imagining a body of mass m falling near the surface of the earth so that r is the earth's radius and the acceleration felt by the body is g. The mass of the earth we call M. Now, simply using these two laws we get:

$$F = mg = \frac{GmM}{r^2}.$$

From these equations we get:

$$M = \frac{r^2 g}{G}.$$

We know the values of everything on the right-hand side of this equation, so we just put them in and arrive at the answer:

$$M = 5.98 \times 10^{24} \text{ kilograms!!}$$

This enormous quantity is the mass of the earth; even expressed in tons it is huge—6.6×10^{21} tons.

Center of Mass

First you learned that it is the sun's gravity that makes the planets travel in orbits about it. Now that you realize that the planets also exert a force on the sun you might logically wonder if the *sun* does not also orbit the *planet*—shades of Ptolemy!—and if the earth does not also orbit the moon. If you do think this, you are right! Naturally the earth, being much heavier than the moon, does not move very much. If you start to try to imagine this picture of the moon going around the earth every twenty-seven days while the earth is at the same time slowly circling the moon, you can see what a complicated situation this is to visualize. Try to make a diagram of *this!* Fortunately the motion *can* be reduced to a much simpler picture.

As the earth and the moon orbit each other with different periods, each body is circling a *moving* center, which is why the motion is so complicated. There does exist, however, one point called the center of mass, which both bodies circle with the *same* period. As seen from each body this point appears to be standing still. Where is this point? It lies between the earth and the moon, and as the earth is moving more slowly than the moon, the center of mass must be nearer the earth. The slower earth thus has the "inside track," with the result that it can complete its orbit in the same time as the faster moon. For any two bodies that are moving about each other we can locate a center of mass from which the motions appear uncomplicated. Figure 5–2 shows this motion.

Finding the Center of Mass

To find the exact position of the center of mass, you can imagine that each body rests on the end of an imaginary weightless seesaw, as in Figure 5–3. The center of mass lies at the point where you would have to place the pivot to make the seesaw balance. As the earth is heavier than the moon, for example, it would have to "sit" much closer to the pivot

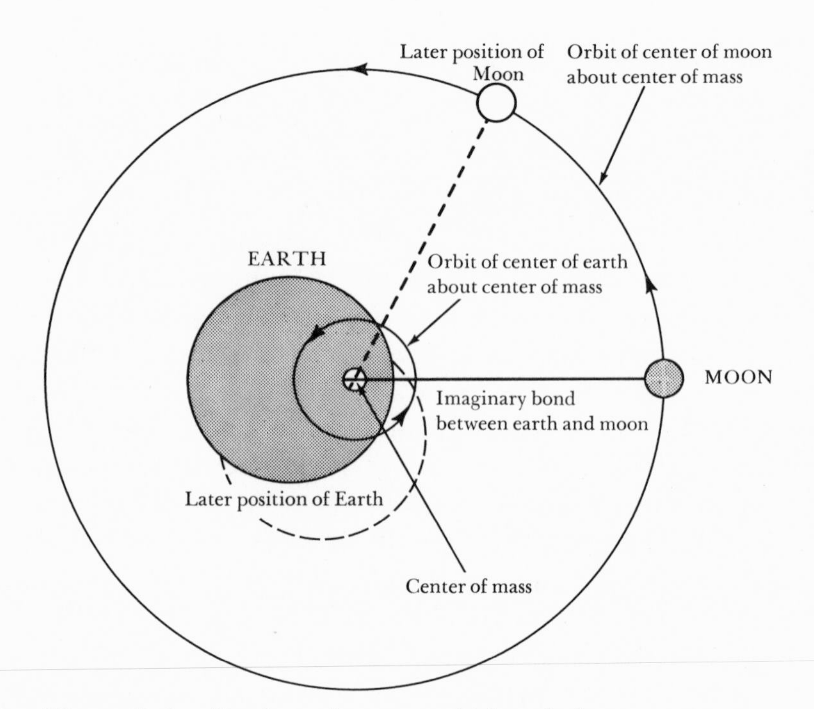

Figure 5–2. Earth and moon orbiting their common center of mass (marked by a cross). The center of the earth follows an orbit as marked around the center of mass while the moon travels in a much larger circle about this center of mass. Earth and moon move as if joined together, like a dumbbell. The solid lines indicate the original position of earth and moon while the broken lines show a later position.

to balance the moon. If we call the distance from the center of the earth to the center of the moon D and the distance from the center of the earth to the center of mass d, the mass of the earth M, and the mass of the moon m, then we can use the so-called balance equation to find d. The equation of balance for a seesaw or any lever gives, in this case, $Md = m(D - d)$. By solving this equation for d we find:

$$d = \left(\frac{m}{m + M}\right) D.$$

Let us calculate the value of d. We found a few pages ago that the mass of the earth is 5.98×10^{24} kilograms; the mass of the moon is 7.34×10^{22} kilograms, and D is 3.84×10^{5} kilometers. Putting these values into the equation above yields a value for d = 4,570 kilometers, the distance from the earth's center to the center of mass. But the earth's radius is greater than this; it is 6,371 kilometers. The center of mass must lie *within* the earth! We were not far from wrong when we assumed earlier that the moon rotated about the earth's center! The same thing is true for the sun. The center

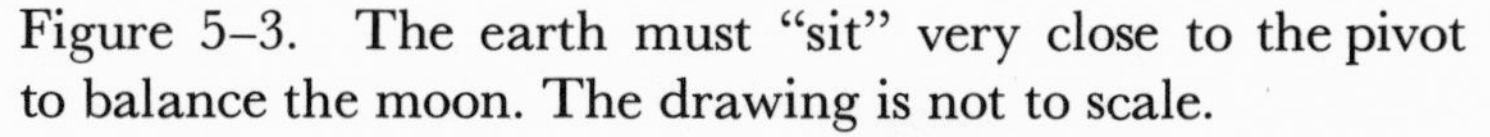

Figure 5–3. The earth must "sit" very close to the pivot to balance the moon. The drawing is not to scale.

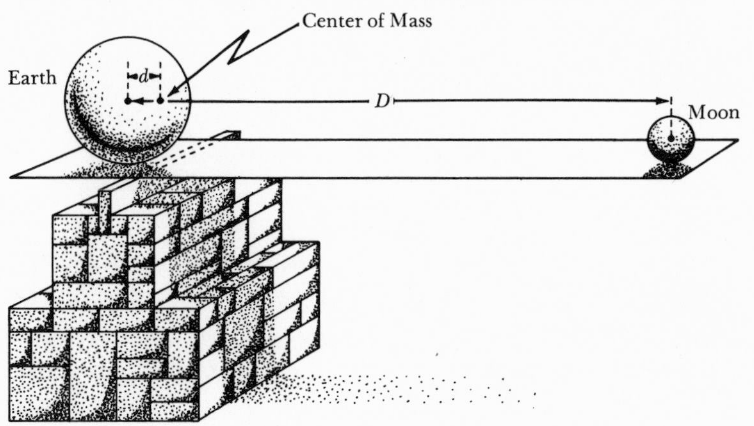

of mass for each sun-planet system lies within the sun, with the exception of Jupiter, because it is so heavy.

The idea of center of mass is very useful in physics. Not only does a group of bodies move about its common center of mass, but also if an outside force is applied to the system of bodies, the system moves as if all the mass were concentrated at the center of mass. The result is that you have to keep track of only one point instead of a system. A single solid body moves as if all its mass were located at the center of mass. This point lies in the center of the body if it is symmetrical and has a constant density. Otherwise you can find the position of the center of mass by a sort of averaging process with the help of calculus or, if you are able, by balancing the body on at least two different points and drawing a plumb line from each balance point. The center of mass, as shown in the sketch, Figure 5–4, lies at the intersection of the lines.

The Period About the Center of Mass

By introducing the notion of center of mass we have replaced the old picture of the moon circling around the earth by a new model. In the new picture the two bodies behave rather like two balls at the ends of a dumbbell, as we saw in Figure 5–2. "Tied" together by gravity, they move together like a dumbbell thrown into the air (if you can imagine *that*), turning end over end about the center of mass. The time taken by the moon to orbit the earth is replaced by the time it takes to orbit the center of mass; these two

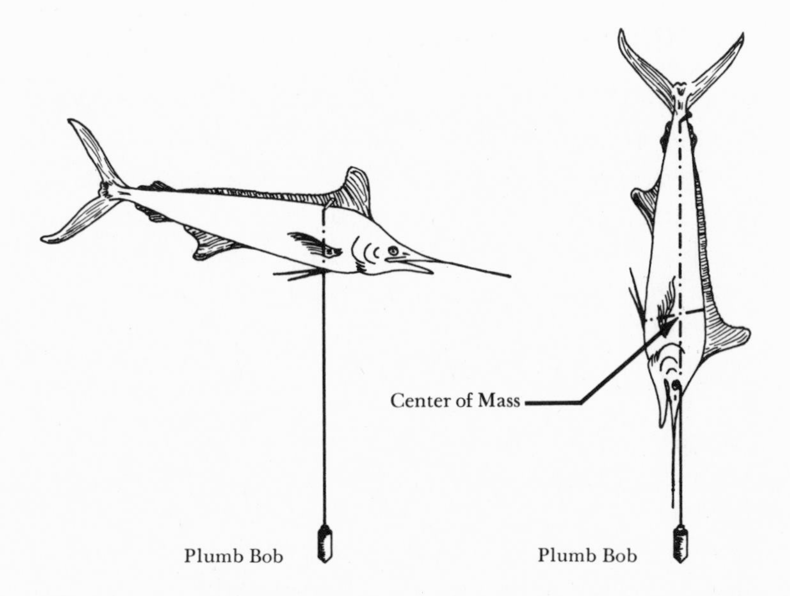

Figure 5–4. Finding the center of mass of an irregularly shaped body. Mark the line made by the string and plumb bob in each position. The center of mass lies underneath the intersection of these two lines.

periods are nearly, but not exactly, the same. The earth also orbits this center of mass in the same amount of time. This period is easy to calculate using the fact that the centrifugal reaction force of each body about the center of mass is equal to the gravitational attraction between them. As you may be a bit sick of seeing calculations by this time, we shall just state that for any two bodies m_1 and m_2 whose centers are a distance r apart, the period of each about their mutual center of mass is found from this equation:

$$(m_1 + m_2)\frac{T^2}{r^3} = \text{constant.}$$

As you remember, Kepler's Third Law (page 39) gave the formula for the period of the planets about the sun. If you compare his law with the formula above, you see that Kepler's Law is not exactly correct, since $(m_1 + m_2)$ has a different value for each planet-sun combination. On the other hand, the masses of the planets are so small compared to the mass of the sun that they can be neglected and then the equation above reduces to: m_1T^2/r^3 = constant. Since the sun's mass m_1 is itself a constant, it can be absorbed into the constant on the right-hand side of the equation. When this is done, we find that the equation becomes T^2/r^3 = constant (not the same constant as the one above, of course). This is the same as the law that Kepler arrived at from observation.

When one deals with bodies that have similar masses it is necessary to use the exact form of the equation that takes into account the masses. We use this equation in a very practical way when by measuring the periods of certain double stars called *binary stars* we are able to determine star masses—one of the very few ways in which we can get an idea of how heavy the stars are.

Binary Stars

It is not easy to weigh the stars which are so far away that it takes a beam of light more than four years to go from the earth to the nearest star! And *nothing* moves faster than light! Yet the astronomers want to know these masses. Luckily a great many stars are close enough together to feel a mutual gravitational attraction and orbit each other. In some cases we can measure the period of these binary stars, and also the distance between their centers. By putting these numbers into the equation in the last section we find the *sum* of the two star masses. This number is not as useless as it may seem, because from it we can at least get an idea of the individual masses. We know that, for one thing, the two masses are not usually very different, so each mass is roughly one half of the sum. Or, taking the extreme case, if we suppose that one mass *is* much larger than the other, then the sum of the masses puts an upper limit to the value of this mass—it is certainly no greater than the sum of the two masses. When nothing at all was known about star masses even such imprecise information as this was a big help. But sometimes observation of binary stars does yield the masses of the *individual* stars. These can be found in those cases where the distances r_1 and r_2 from the stars to the center of mass can be observed, as sometimes happens. In that case the ratio m_1/m_2 can be found from the lever equation ($m_1/m_2 = r_2/r_1$). Knowing both the sum and the ratio of the masses, it is very simple to solve these two equations for the two unknown values of m_1 and m_2. Quite a few star masses have been found in this way. This procedure yielded still more fruit when astronomers found that there is a relationship between the mass of a star and its luminosity (brightness). Using the values they already knew for the mass and luminosity of the binary stars, they could plot a curve on a graph. From this curve the masses of other stars can be found simply by measuring their luminosity! Curiously enough, although the stars vary enormously in dimensions, temperature, and density, their masses fall into the very small range of about one tenth of the sun's mass to ten times the sun's mass.

The Discovery of Neptune and Pluto

Not only do heavenly bodies interact with their visible neighbors; sometimes they are affected by their unseen fellow space travelers as well. In that case their odd motions give away the presence of the other body. In this way Neptune was discovered.

After the planet Uranus was found by accident in 1781, astronomers kept it under observation for several years to plot its orbit. Taking into account the interaction of this planet with the sun, and also with its nearest neighbors, Saturn and Jupiter, the astronomers were able to predict its future path. Such was their faith in Newton's theory of gravitation and in their calculations that they were hardly surprised to find the planet appearing reliably where it was supposed to be with the predictability of an ocean cruise liner making stops at port after port on schedule, for forty years. Then, to the dismay of all, Uranus slowly drifted away from this expected orbit until the scientists were obliged to go over their calculations. They found no errors, and so they came to the conclusion either that Newton was wrong or—an unseen heavenly body was pulling Uranus out of its proper path. Two astronomers, Urbain Leverrier in France and John Couch Adams in England, went through the formidable amount of work that was required to find the position and mass of a body that could produce the observed distortion of Uranus' path. Adams sent his results to England's Astronomer Royal with the hope that someone on his staff would try to find the hidden body. This gentleman apparently had more important things on his mind, and he put aside Adams' paper. Meanwhile Leverrier had sent his work to a young German astronomer, Johann Galle, who in 1846 quickly found a faint body very near to the place predicted by Leverrier. This turned out to be the eighth planet, which was given the name of Neptune. Meanwhile the Astronomer Royal also located the planet where Adams had predicted it should be. Leverrier and Adams share the credit for this discovery.

When Neptune also began to stray from its predicted orbit, it was natural to assume the existence of still another planet. The deviations were so small, however, that it was very difficult to pinpoint the new planet's position. It was not until 1930 that the planet was found, lying so far from the sun that it was in outer darkness. The planet was named Pluto, after the god of the underworld who also spent his life in darkness. The first two letters of Pluto's name are the same as the initials of the American astronomer Percival Lowell. Lowell was one of the first scientists to try to predict the position of the planet, but it was not found until after his death.

Pluto is so far away that it is difficult to measure its dimensions, but it is apparently much smaller and lighter than its nearest planetary neighbors, Uranus and Neptune. Pluto's small size and peculiar orbit, which cuts inside that of Neptune, has suggested to some astronomers that Pluto may be an escaped former

THE SOLAR SYSTEM

Body	*Average distance from sun (in millions of miles)*	*Average diameter (thousands of miles)*	*Mass compared to that of earth (number of times the mass of earth)*	*Period of revolution*[a]
Sun		865	333,000	
Moon	[f]	2.16	0.01	27⅓ days
Mercury	36	3	0.05	88 days
Venus	67	7.7	0.82	225 days
Earth	93	7.9	1.00	365 days
Mars	142	4.2	0.11	687 days
Jupiter	483	89	318	12 years
Saturn	887	75	95	29 years
Uranus	1,784	31	15	84 years
Neptune	2,795	28	17	165 years
Pluto	3,672	8?	0.9?	248 years

[a] Orbital period.
[b] Spin period.
[c] Density of water $= 1.0\ g/cm^3$.
[d] $1\ g = 32\ ft/sec^2 = 9.8\ m/sec^2$.

moon of Neptune. More evidence is needed before we can be sure if that theory is correct, and the great distance of Pluto makes this evidence very hard to obtain.

Period of rotation[b]	*Mean density, g/cm*^{3}[c]	*Acceleration of gravity, g*[d]	*Escape velocity, miles/sec*[e]	*Known satellites*
25–30 days	1.4	28	383	(9 planets)
27⅓ days	3.4	0.2	1.2	—
88 days	5	0.4	2.7	0
257 days[g]	5.0	0.9	6.5	0
24 hr	5.5	1.0	7.0	1
24.6 hr	4.0	0.4	3.2	2
9.8 hr	1.3	2.7	38	12
10.3 hr	0.7	1.2	23	9
10.8 hr[h]	1.5	1.0	14	5
15.7 hr	2.0	1.4	16	2
16 hr(?)	5?	?	?	0

[e] Speed necessary for permanent escape from gravitational field of the body.
[f] The mean distance of the moon from the earth is 238,000 miles.
[g] The direction of rotation of Venus is opposite to that of the other planets.
[h] The axis of rotation of Uranus is only 8° from the plane of its orbit.

chapter six

MEASURING THE ACCELERATION OF GRAVITY

Although we have said that *g*, the acceleration of gravity near the earth, is 32 feet per second per second, it is not true that *g* has this value at every point on the earth's surface. Different geological situations provide local distributions which are slightly different from the average all over the earth. Mountains, trenches in the sea, the sea itself, and certain mineral deposits are some of the features of the earth's crust that produce a local variation in the value of *g*. Another change occurs because the earth's shape is not truly spherical, but is slightly flattened at the poles. Because the earth's surface is closer to its center at the poles than at the equator, *g* is greater at the poles than at the equator. In this chapter you will read about methods used to measure *g* and the ways in which these determinations are put to practical use.

To measure *g*, or any other quantity for that matter, you first look for phenomena which depend on *g* and then design experiments around them. For example, as Galileo's classic experiment showed, the motion of a falling body depends directly on *g*. This fact is used in one of the modern ways of finding a very accurate value for *g*.

When we measure g we are not actually measuring the acceleration due to gravity alone. This is because the "gravity" of the earth consists of two parts. The main part is that which comes from the gravitational attraction between bodies. The second part is the "centrifugal" acceleration caused by the earth's rotation. This rotational acceleration depends on the latitude on the earth's surface; it is least at the poles, while at the equator it reaches the by no means negligible value of ⅓ of one percent of the first part. As both accelerations are directed along the line between the centers of the earth and of the body, they would be inseparable except that we can easily calculate the centrifugal acceleration for any point on the earth and subtract this from the measured value of g.

The pseudogravity caused by rotation of a body is put to good use in the design of spaceships, where an artificial gravity can be provided by having the spaceship rotate about an axis which passes through itself.

Types of Measurement

It is not our intention here to give precise descriptions of existing apparatus used for measuring the acceleration of gravity. For one thing, techniques change with the passing of time so that a method you learn about now might well be obsolete before you could use it. Nor could any of this equipment be built at home. Very high accuracy is needed in these determinations and the apparatus is correspondingly precise. On the other hand, it is interesting to survey the types of apparatus that are being used now to arrive at a value of g.

The measurement of g may be performed on a body in motion (this is called a dynamic method), or on a body at rest (static method). Determinations of g using a pendulum, or timing the fall of a body, are examples of the first method. Static determinations of g are obtained from the use of a sophisticated version of the spring balance or from a device called a gas-pressure gravimeter. Some instruments yield an absolute value for g; others give only the difference between the value at the point being measured and the value at a base station.

Pendulum Method

The time needed for a pendulum to complete one swing depends, as Galileo observed many years ago, not on the weight of the bob, but only on the length of the wire supporting it. To find out the exact relationship between the period T of a pendulum and the length L of the wire, we work with a so-called mathematical pendulum, Figure 6–1, an imaginary combination of a body of minute size hanging from a weightless cord. The weight of the body does not affect the period. The calculations yield an approximate period for this ideal pendulum of

$$T = 2\pi\sqrt{\frac{L}{g}}.$$

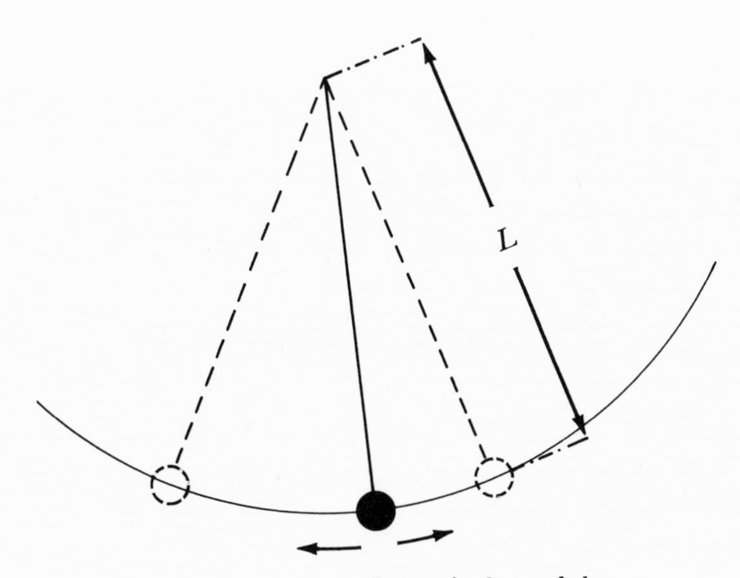

Figure 6–1. A mathematical pendulum.

We say an *approximate* period because this formula is correct only for small angles of swing; the smaller the angles the more nearly accurate becomes the equation. For gravity measurements the pendulum is allowed to swing through angles of only several minutes (one degree equals 60 minutes). Even so, correction terms have to be added. If you solve the equation for g you get

$$g = \frac{4\pi^2 L}{T^2}.$$

If one could somehow get a perfect mathematical pendulum, it would be easy to determine g simply by measuring L and then timing a small swing of the pendulum to get T. In the real world the situation is more complicated. We must work with real, not ideal pendulums. Any body suspended at some point so that it can swing is a pendulum. The suspension point need not lie outside the body as it does in the mathematical pendulum. The body may very well be pivoted about a point lying inside itself, as in Figure 6–2. We can consider the body as being made up of an infinite number of mathematical pendulums; an equivalent pendulum can then be found. This is the one mathematical pendulum that has the same period as the body. In determining *g*, one uses for *L* not the real length of the pendulum, nor the distance from pivot to either end,

Figure 6–2. A real, or physical, pendulum. This irregularly shaped body is suspended at point *O* within itself. It has the same period as its equivalent pendulum of length *L* shown here. This period is the same if the pendulum is suspended from *X* instead of from *O*.

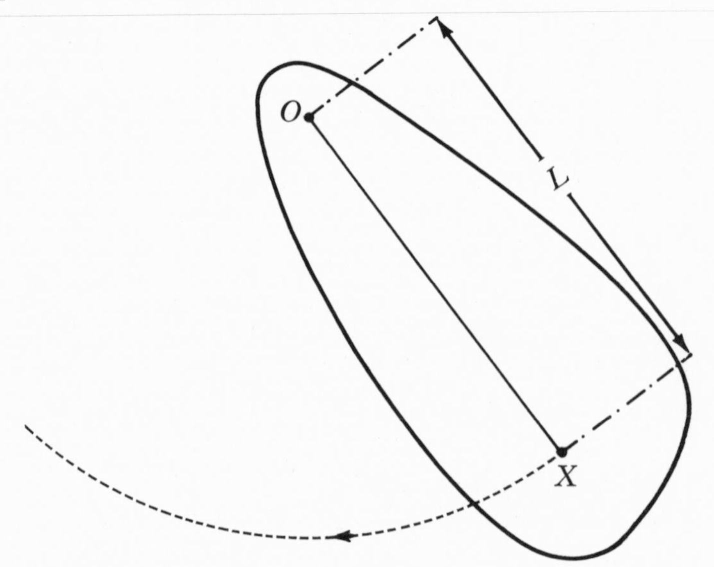

or to the center of mass; the L in the equation is the length of the equivalent pendulum.

Because extremely precise values of g are needed, the scientist must eliminate sources of small error such as fluctuations in the air pressure (the determination is carried out in a vacuum), temperature changes (which affect the measurements by changing the length of the pendulum), and even the flexing of the pendulum's stand. This last source of error is very hard to cope with; it happens when the swinging pendulum sets its own support in motion. The moving stand in turn transmits this motion to the pendulum and changes the period. In practice the pendulum apparatus is very complicated.

Falling Body Method

The theory of this method of finding g is straightforward. The acceleration of gravity is found from the equation for falling bodies worked out by Galileo. This is

$$d = \frac{gt^2}{2},$$

from which we get

$$g = \frac{2d}{t^2}.$$

The difficulty of this method comes in measuring accurately the time required for the body to fall and the distance d through which it falls. Great accuracy has been achieved by the following procedure. A stick one or two meters long falls in a vacuum past a camera which is synchronized with a light that flashes ten times per second. The camera films that part of the scale which is in front of it each time the light goes on, that is, every tenth of a second. The result is a record of the distance fallen per tenth of a second. Precision is assured by calibrating the measuring stick against the international standard meter and by measuring the times between the flashes against a standard frequency signal. This apparatus is shown schematically in Figure 6–3.

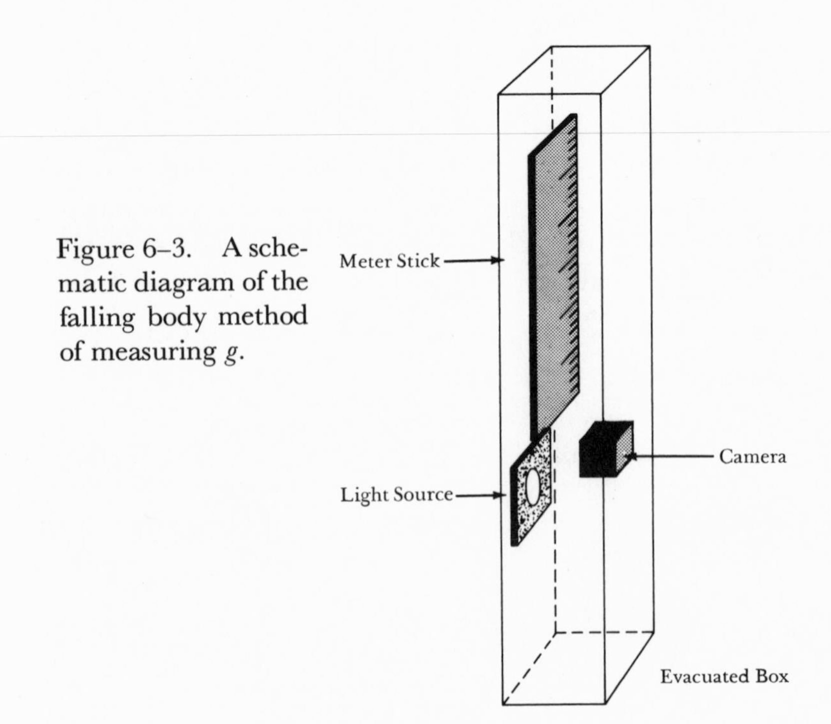

Figure 6–3. A schematic diagram of the falling body method of measuring *g*.

The Gas-Pressure Gravimeter

Air pressure is measured in a barometer by the height to which the mercury column within rises. This height depends on the air pressure, but also on the density of mercury and the acceleration of gravity g. As the last two quantities are known, the height of the mercury column can be calibrated to give air pressure directly. Suppose now that we were to turn this process around. If the mercury column were sealed off from contact with the outside air pressure and were instead joined to a closed volume of gas whose pressure could be held constant, the only changes in its height would be due to changes in g. If this device were moved from place to place, changes in the level of mercury would reflect different values of g. This is the principle behind the gas-pressure gravimeter which measures relative values of g with respect to a base value. The instrument is not very accurate, and its chief worth lies in work at sea where the motion of the ship affects the precision of pendulum meters.

Balance Gravimeters

When a weight is hung from a spring, the spring becomes longer. How much longer it becomes depends on a quantity called the spring constant c (the stiffer the spring, the greater the value of c) and the amount of weight mg. This change in length is

$$s = \frac{mg}{c}.$$

By measuring the change in the elongation produced by the same weight in the same spring moved to different places, one can arrive at a comparison of the values of g at those places. See Figure 6–4. As the changes in length due to changes in g are small, the main difficulty in using this method is to find a way to magnify the elongations. Sensitive and cheap versions of this

Figure 6–4. Elongation of a spring. The first elongation s occurs when the body of mass m is placed on the end of the spring. The second change in length, shown here greatly exaggerated as an elongation s', occurs when the same spring with the same mass is moved to a different location where the local value of g is greater. The spring would become shorter instead of longer if g_2 were less than g_1. The change in length s' is very small and its measurement presents problems.

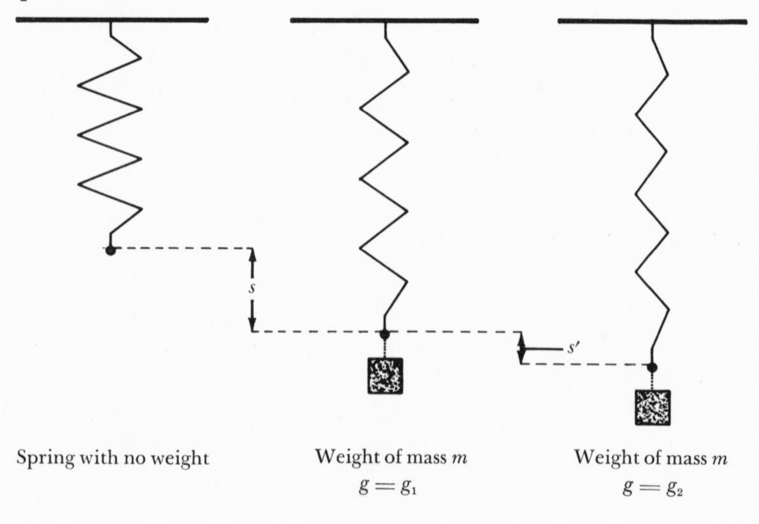

gravimeter have been developed and are used in petroleum prospecting.

Prospecting

The density of the earth's surface varies from place to place according to what is to be found there—rock, chalk, water, salt, gold. These density differences produce local variations in the value of g. By measuring g in various locations, hidden mineral deposits may be discovered. Prospectors have found the gravity survey to be a useful technique. The deposits will not show up in a survey unless there is either a large enough deposit to affect the local value of g or a sharp enough difference in density between deposit and surrounding crust to affect g. For this reason gravity surveys are more useful in discovering oil fields than in finding most metallic minerals, even though there is a greater density difference between the metallic ore and its surroundings than between the petroleum deposit and its surroundings. The oil deposit is usually so much bigger than the ore deposit that its larger size more than makes up for its smaller density difference. A salt dome is sometimes associated with petroleum accumulations. The salt has a lower density than the crust in its vicinity, so a gravity minimum points the way to a possible oil field.

Gravity surveys are also helpful in finding deposits of very dense materials such as magnetite, chromite, and barium which, even though there may be a relatively small amount of mineral present, will give values of g much higher than the value in the vicinity.

Undersea Trenches

Gravity surveys play a role in describing the unseen depths of the oceans. The floors of the seas are by no means flat; they contain mountains, valleys, and plateaus. In certain places there are huge trenches where we find the greatest depths of the oceans. Most of these trenches are in the Pacific Ocean, as are the three deepest, the Marianas Trench, the Japan Trench, and the Tonga Trench, each about 10.8 kilometers below sea level. The existence of these underwater chasms was detected by several means, including the gravity survey. The depths give their presence away by producing large "negative" gravity readings on the surface, that is, gravity readings lower than average. Less dramatic features of the ocean floor can also be located with the help of gravity surveys: valleys, faults, folds are among these invisible parts of the sea floor.

The study of gravity has taken us far from the simple consideration of falling bodies. We have just seen that the value of something as apparently irrelevant as the acceleration of gravity can help us to "see" below the surface of the earth and of the sea. In the next chapter we shall return to the motion of falling bodies and the study of them, which is called *ballistics.*

chapter seven BALLISTICS

Knowing only what Galileo learned about gravity and mechanics, we can develop the science of *ballistics.* As ballistics is the study of the path of a projectile moving in a gravitational field, and as a good example of such a projectile is a cannon-ball, it is not surprising to find that Galileo's patron, the war-embroiled Duke of Tuscany, encouraged Galileo's studies in this field.

There is a straightforward experiment that illustrates a great simplification in the study of projectiles, the separation of their motion into two components. Two identical balls go off the edge of the table shown in Figure 7–1 at the same time. One ball simply falls off the edge, while the other is pushed so that it goes flying off at high speed. Which ball hits the ground first? The answer is that, although they touch at different spots, the two balls hit the ground at exactly the same time. What this means is that we can consider the vertical and the horizontal parts of the velocity as completely separate from each other. The horizontal part of the velocity of the second ball came from the fact that it was already moving horizontally when it left the table, and so by Newton's First Law it continued to do so. It

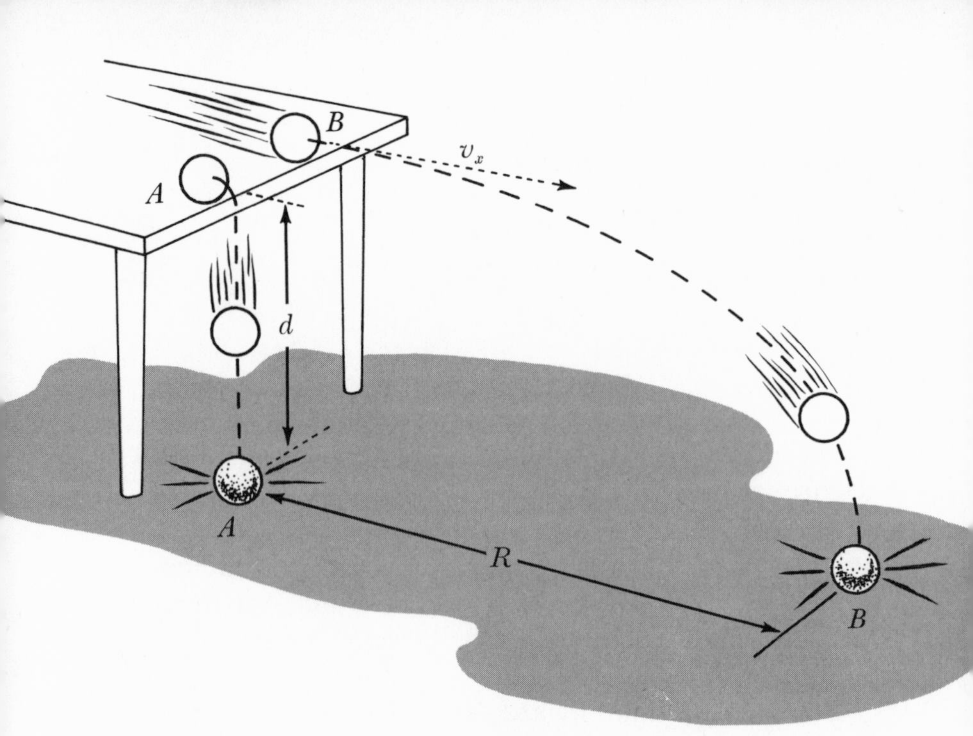

Figure 7–1. Two balls A and B, falling simultaneously from the edge of a table. Ball B has an initial velocity. Which ball hits the ground first? As you can see, both balls hit simultaneously, although in different spots.

was only the vertical component of the motion that was affected by gravity, and both balls were affected by the same amount, which explains why they took the same amount of time to fall. See Figure 7–2. This separation into vertical and horizontal components can be performed on forces, accelerations, velocities, or on any *vector* quantity, that is, any quantity that has a direction associated with it as well as an amount or magnitude.

Resolution of Velocity Into Its Components

The horizontal and vertical components of velocity or any other vector are easy to find. If we measure the angle formed by the direction of the vector with the horizontal and call it θ, a Greek letter often used to label angles, and if we label the magnitude of the velocity v (the magnitude of velocity is usually called speed), the two components are given by these two equations:

$$\text{horizontal component} = v_x = v \text{ cosine } \theta$$
$$\text{vertical component} = v_y = v \text{ sine } \theta.$$

You may already have learned the meanings of the words "sine" and "cosine" of an angle. If not, it does

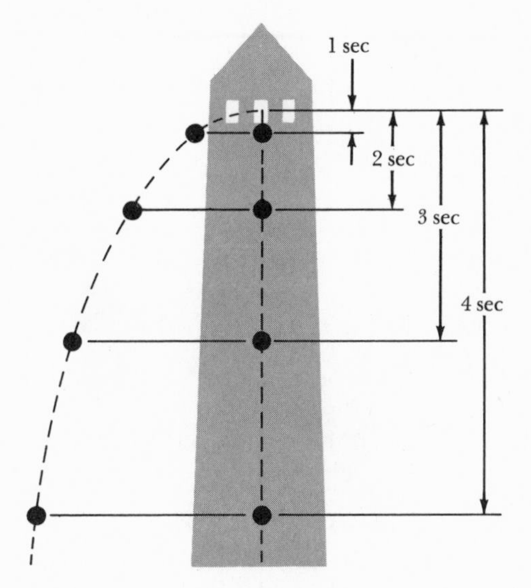

Figure 7–2. Vertical motion is independent of horizontal motion.

not matter; the explanation is quickly given. If we have a right triangle such as that in Figure 7–3, we can define the sines and the cosines of the angles A and B in terms of the sides of the triangle. The sine of an angle is equal to the side opposite it divided by the hypotenuse. The cosine of an angle is equal to the side next to it which is not the hypotenuse, divided by the hypotenuse. For this triangle the sine of A (written "sin A") is equal to a/c while the cosine of A (cos A) is

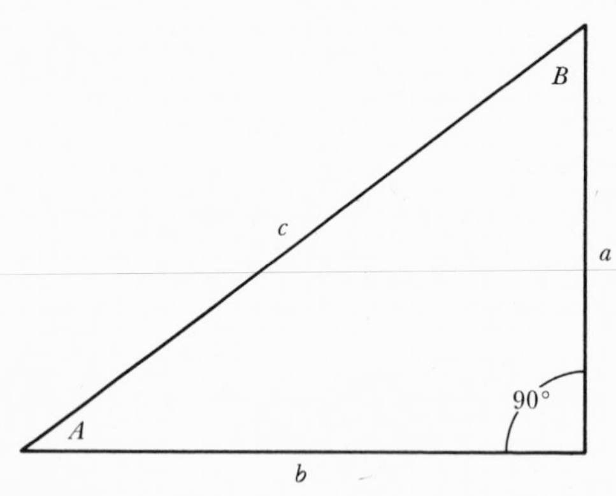

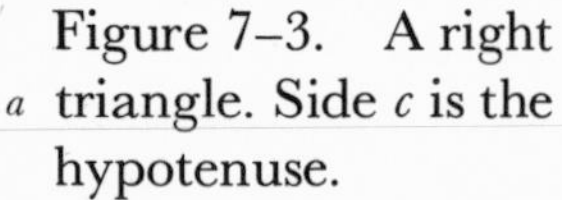
Figure 7–3. A right triangle. Side c is the hypotenuse.

b/c. For angle B we find $\sin B = b/c$ and $\cos B = a/c$. If we pick a triangle whose hypotenuse is 1, then when we have specified the angle, the other two sides are automatically specified also. For example, if $A = 30°$ and the hypotenuse is 1, a must equal ½ while b must equal $\sqrt{3}/2$ or .866. Therefore the sine of $30° = .500$ and the cosine $= .866$. The sines and cosines of all angles from 0° to 90° are given in tables and are simple to look up: they are always less than or equal to 1.

Imagine that a ball is moving at a 45° angle from the horizontal with a speed of ten miles per hour. We find the vertical and horizontal components of its velocity by using the equations above. The sine and the cosine of 45° are equal to each other and $= 1/\sqrt{2}$ or .707. From the equation then $v_x = (10)(.707) =$ 7.07 miles per hour and v_y also equals 7.07 miles per hour. Although we have used velocity as an example of a vector resolved into its components, the same procedure is followed with any other vector, for example, force or acceleration.

Why Resolve Vectors Into Their Components?

Why do we go to the trouble of resolving vectors into their components? We can answer this with the help of Figure 7–1. The path of the second ball is not a straight line but a curve which is called a *parabola.* Because the direction of the velocity is always changing, it is hard to describe the motion. Now if we can break this curved line into two straight lines, as we can by resolving the velocity vector, we have made our problem easier. The separation splits the velocity into a part along the force of gravity and a part perpendicular to it.

Falling Balls

Let us calculate now some specific numbers which describe the paths taken by the two balls. First of all, we have said that the two balls take exactly the same time to reach the floor. What is this time? To answer this we must refer to the equation on page 56: $d = gt^2/2$. If we solve this equation for t, we find the time it takes a body to fall a distance d is

$$t = \sqrt{\frac{2d}{g}}.$$

The table is 75 centimeters high; if we put this value into the equation, we get a falling time of .39 seconds. This is the time it takes each of the two balls to reach the floor.

The next question we ask is how fast the first ball is moving when it hits the ground. The only factor contributing to its motion is gravity. This force makes the ball move 9.8 meters per second faster during each second that it is falling. We express this in an equation from page 55, $v = at$ (since the initial speed is zero). The acceleration a is the acceleration of gravity g, and when we use this value we get for the speed $v = gt = (9.8)\ (.39) = 3.8$ meters per second, or 12.4 feet per second.

The second ball has two contributions to its final speed. There is first of all the effect of gravity which makes it go faster and faster toward the ground, just as does the first ball. In addition the ball had an initial velocity of, let us say, 5 meters per second (which corresponds to 10.8 miles per hour) in the horizontal direction. We wish to know the total final speed. Do we add up the two speeds, 3.8 meters per second and 5 meters per second? The answer is an emphatic NO. The trouble is that we are not adding *speeds,* we are adding velocities, which are vectors. Vectors cannot be added like ordinary numbers; they are not ordinary numbers. To find the sum of the two velocities you must perform a vector addition.

Addition of Vectors

It is easiest to visualize vector addition when the vectors are forces. The force F_y in Figure 7–4 is pulling vertically while the force F_x is pulling hori-

Figure 7–4. Addition of vectors. F is the vector sum of F_x and F_y. It is located by drawing perpendicular lines (dotted in the diagram) from the tip of each vector being added. The resultant F goes from the origin to the intersection of the dotted lines. The other diagonal of the rectangle that is formed, F', is equal to F and forms a right triangle with F_x and F_y. This allows us to find the length of F' and therefore of F by using the Pythagorean Theorem: $F_x^2 + F_y^2 = F^2$.

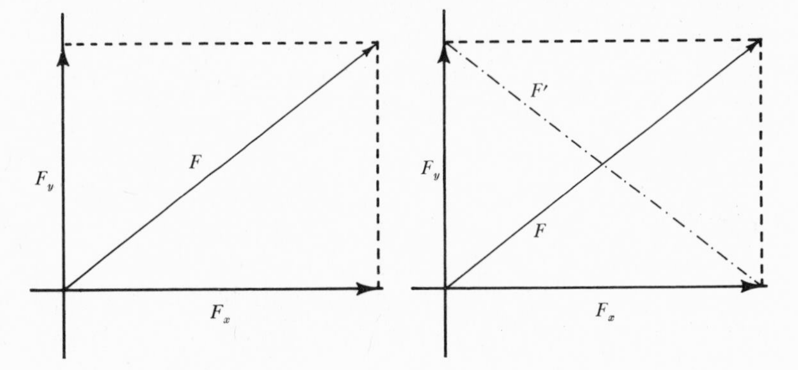

zontally. The resultant force F is in the direction shown in the picture, as you would expect. F is the *vector* sum of F_x and F_y. We would like to know the magnitude of F. The length of F is the same as that of the dotted line from the tip of F_x to the tip of F_y since they are two diagonals of the same rectangle. The dotted line F' forms a right triangle with F_x and F_y so we can use the Pythagorean Theorem to find its length. This theorem tells us that the sum of the squares of the sides of a right triangle equals the square of the hypotenuse. This gives us the equation we need to find F:

$$F^2 = F_x^2 + F_y^2$$

$$F = \sqrt{F_x^2 + F_y^2}.$$

These equations are true for all vectors. In the case of the velocity of the second ball as it hit the ground, we find that the vector sum of its velocities is

$$v = \sqrt{v_x^2 + v_y^2}$$

$$v = \sqrt{(5)^2 + (3.8)^2} = 6.28 \text{ meters per second.}$$

When it hits the ground the ball is moving at an angle to the horizon, as you can see from the illustration, Figure 7–5. This angle is found from the fact that $\cos \theta = v_x/v$. In this case $\cos \theta = 5/6.28 = .79$. The angle that corresponds to this cosine is 37°.

Range

The first ball falls right below the edge of the table. Where does the second ball land? To find out this distance, which is called the *range,* we make use of the fact that motion in the horizontal direction is independent of motion in the vertical direction. On the other hand, we can use the time of falling which we found by considering the vertical motion to determine the horizontal range. This ball was falling for .39 seconds. To put this another way, the ball was in the air for .39 seconds and in this time it was moving horizontally as well as vertically. No horizontal force, except air resistance which we are neglecting, acted to accelerate or decelerate the ball during this time, so that it had a constant horizontal speed of 5 meters per second. Since the speed is constant, we can use the equation $d = v_x t$ to calculate the distance. To prevent confusion with the vertical distance d we shall now call this distance R, the range, and get:

$$R = (5)\,(.39) = 1.95 \text{ meters.}$$

The second ball falls 1.95 meters away from the edge of

Figure 7–5. The velocity of the second ball of Figure 7–1 as it hits the ground. It is easy to see that $v^2 = v_x{}^2 + v_y{}^2$.

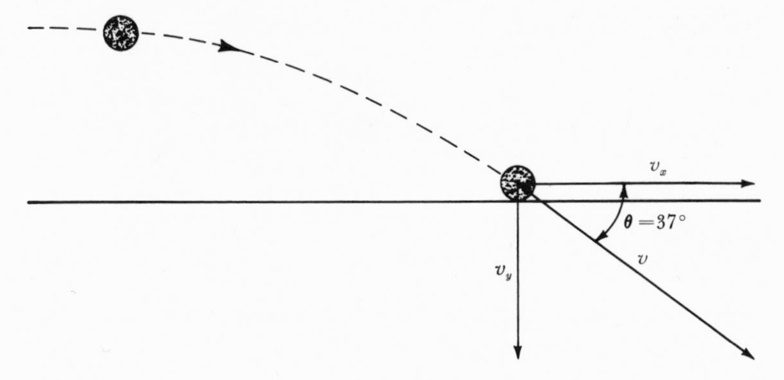

the table. The total distance it travels along the parabolic curve is considerably more than this, however.

The path of a bomb falling from an airplane is like that of the second ball in Figure 7–1. The bomb has an initial velocity equal to the plane's velocity when the bomb was dropped. Like the ball, the bomb does not fall straight down, but instead travels in a curved path.

Skyrockets and Other Projectiles

Even a body that is shot up away from the earth is a "falling body." As the body moves upward, gravity is constantly acting on it so that it falls at the same time. This is what happens in the flight of a skyrocket or a signaling flare. Let us imagine that we celebrate the Fourth of July by setting off a skyrocket at an angle of 45°. See Figure 7–6. It goes shooting up with a speed of 300 feet per second. How high would it rise if there were no air resistance? To answer this, we first find out how long it takes to reach the highest point of its path. We begin by separating the initial velocity into its components. The horizontal component $v_x = 300 \cos 45° = 212$ feet per second; the vertical component is the same, since $\sin 45° = \cos 45°$. The rocket's vertical speed is made up of two parts: it is rising with a speed v_y of 212 feet per second, but it is simultaneously falling with an ever-increasing speed produced by gravity. This speed v_g grows by 32 feet per second each second that the skyrocket is in the air, so that $v_g = gt$. A time comes when v_g becomes as large as

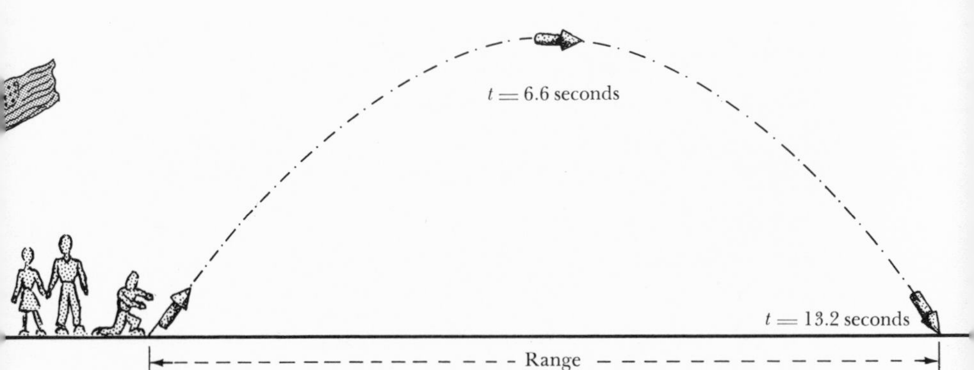

Figure 7–6. The motion of a skyrocket (not shown to scale).

v_y but in the opposite direction. The net speed of the rocket is then zero; it comes to a stop and then begins to fall back to the earth. We find the time when this occurs by setting the two speeds equal and then solving for t. This yields the equation $gt = 212$ feet per second; therefore $t = 6.6$ seconds. The rocket takes the same amount of time to fall from the top of its trajectory to the ground, so it is in the air a total of 13.2 seconds.

To find out the highest altitude reached by the rocket, we write an equation for the height at any time t. Like the speed, the height is made up of two parts, the distance traveled upward at a constant rate of 212 feet per second and, subtracted from it, the distance fallen under gravity, $gt^2/2$. This gives the general equation for the height of a projectile at any time t after it was launched:

$$h = v_y t - \frac{gt^2}{2}.$$

When we substitute the values of v_y and the time to reach the top of the path for this skyrocket, we find that $h = (212)\ (6.6) - (16)\ (6.6)^2 = 702$ feet—the highest point reached by the rocket.

Range

We find the range for this skyrocket as we did that of the second ball. Its horizontal speed is constant and equal to v_x or 212 feet per second. The rocket is in the air during 13.2 seconds. The distance it travels from where we launched it is then $R = v_x t = (212)\ (13.2) = 2{,}798$ feet.

In general, the formula for the range of a projectile (obtained by combining all the steps we have just followed) is

$$R = \frac{2v_0^2 \sin\theta \cos\theta}{g}$$

where v_0 is the initial velocity of the projectile and θ the angle between the velocity and the horizontal. This equation tells us something interesting about the maximum range: this is greatest when $\sin\theta \cos\theta$ is greatest. From trigonometry you will learn that $2 \sin\theta \cos\theta = \sin 2\theta$. The largest value the sine of an angle can reach is 1, which is the sine of 90°. Therefore the range is greatest when 2θ is 90° or when θ is 45°. Try sending paper gliders off at 45°, or aiming water pistols at this angle. This works quite well, and would work even better if it were not for the effect of air resistance. To overcome this drag you should aim a bit higher.

Rockets

You must have noticed on television that rockets are launched vertically upward. The scientists who send off these missiles are not trying for maximum range; they are hoping to get the rocket up and away from the effects of the earth's air resistance, from disturbance of crosswinds, and from the effect of the gravitational force as soon as possible. Even at a height above the earth of twenty miles the rocket still feels a force of gravity equal to 99 percent that on the earth. Air resistance increases rapidly with high speeds, so an important branch of rocketry is the design of a shape that presents the minimum of resistance to the air.

This chapter summarized the effects of the *earth's* gravity on objects on or near the earth. The moon is close enough to exert a gravitational pull on bodies on earth also. This force is so small as to be negligible except for its effect on the earth itself, which is deformed slightly by the mutual force. The rigid earth resists this deformation, but the oceans slide more easily in response to the gravitational attraction. The result is the tides—the subject of our next chapter.

chapter eight

THE TIDES AND PRECESSION

Like a great dumbbell the earth and the moon turn together end over end. Kept apart by their rotation, held together by their mutual attraction, the system of two bodies is in perfect balance. What if we do not look at the system as a whole but instead inspect certain parts of it? Specifically, what forces are acting on the regions of the earth nearest the moon and on those farthest away, *A* and *B* in Figure 8–1? As it is about 4,000 miles from the center of the earth, *A* feels more lunar gravitational attraction than does the center. What little centrifugal reaction force there is about the center of mass (which lies very close to *A*) is in the same direction as the gravitational force, and *A* moves toward the moon. At *B* the situation is just the opposite. There the lunar attraction is less than at the center of the earth while the centrifugal force is greater, so *B* moves away from the moon. At other locations on the earth similar struggles between gravity and centrifugal force are taking place, although the effect is strongest at *A* and at *B* which are in line with the moon. The slight football-shaped deformation that you see (greatly exaggerated) in Figure 8–1 is the result of these unbalanced forces.

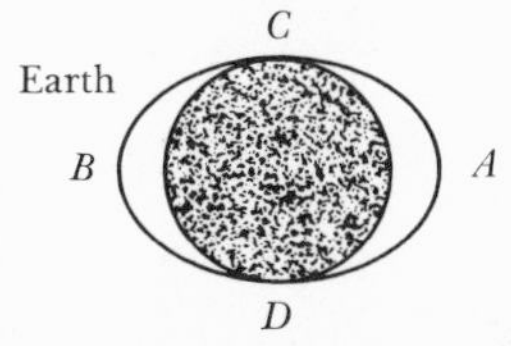

Figure 8–1. The deformation of the earth as a result of lunar gravitational attraction.

The earth is rigid and resists being pulled like taffy, although it does move a certain amount. It is much easier for the oceans to move; they pile up on the sides facing away from the moon and facing it to produce the tides.

Solar Tides

The tides in the ocean are made up of a solar tide as well as a lunar tide. Although the sun also changes the shape of the earth and pulls up tides, its effect is only about half as great as that of the moon. At first glance it seems curious that the sun should produce a smaller effect than the moon even though the gravitational attraction of the sun on the earth is about two hundred times that of the moon. However, the tide-producing force is not a straightforward gravitational attraction, and it is found to depend on the inverse *cube* of the distance. The sun is 390 times as far from the earth as is the moon. When this number appears *cubed* in the denominator of the formula for tide-producing force, even the sun's enormous mass of 26.6 million times the mass of the moon cannot cancel its effect. In the expression for gravitational attraction this distance is only squared in the denominator and the sun's mass more than compensates.

Spring Tides and Neap Tides

About twice a month, when the sun, moon, and earth are in line, the solar tide is added to the lunar tide to produce the abnormally large bulge known as the *spring tide.* This is shown in Figure 8–2a, while Figure 8–2b shows the diminished tides that occur when the sun and the moon form a right angle with the earth. Some of the distortion is toward the sun, some toward the moon, and so neither tide can be as high as when the two are added together. The resulting diminished tide is called the *neap tide.* During the spring tide *high water* is unusually high and *low water* unusually low, while at neap tide the difference between high and low water is less than average.

Tidal Prediction

It should be a simple matter to predict the times and heights of the high and low tides that occur at any location on the coasts. As the earth turns on its axis, a given place on it will face the moon and face away from the moon about once a day. At these two times we should expect a high tide. When the earth has turned so that this location is at *C* or *D* in Figure 8–1 with respect to the moon, we expect low tides. Throughout the day, therefore, any point on the earth

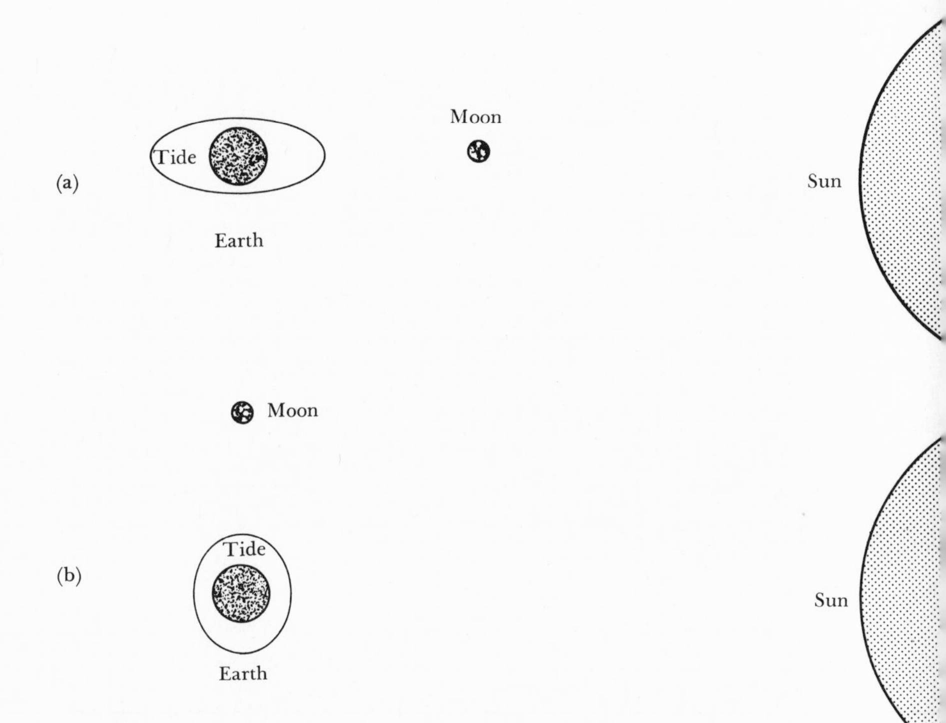

Figure 8–2. Spring tides (a) occur when the moon and the sun are in line and their effects are added together. The highest and the lowest tides are at this time. Neap tides (b) occur when the moon and the sun form a right angle with the earth and the tide is distributed between both directions. The moon raises a higher tide than does the sun but neither effect is very large. The difference between high tide and low tide is less than usual.

should experience two high and two low tides whose heights should be the same each day.

As you have realized by now, nothing is that simple

in the real world. The first complication in this picture comes from the fact that the angle between the sun and the moon with the earth keeps changing during the month. The result is not only the phenomenon of the spring and neap tides but also an alteration of the height of tides at times in between. It is still possible to calculate the tides since the positions of the sun and moon are known throughout the month, but our picture has already lost its simplicity. A greater difficulty comes from the friction of the seas moving against the irregular coasts and ocean bottoms. It is hardly possible to calculate *this* delaying force which changes from place to place, nor to compute the slowing down or speeding up of the crest of the tide as it meets shoals or deeps. Another factor that affects the tide is the friction of the earth rotating beneath the oceans, the subject of our next section. Even the weather changes the height of the tide from what we could expect from the original picture. A strong wind pushes the water ahead of it, just as it would push snow into drifts, and raises the water level on the weather shore.

Anyone who has to do with the sea—fishermen, merchant marine, naval personnel, yachtsmen must know the times and heights of high and low tide. In seas like the Mediterranean and the Baltic where the tide may be measured in inches, their need is hardly great, but in places where the tides may be thirty or forty feet, off the coast of Brittany, for example, or off Nova Scotia, the navigator of a vessel cannot make a mistake. Ignorance of the tides can make him drive his ship aground, can keep him from taking advantage of a favorable tidal current, or can force him to lengthen his voyage because his ship must fight an unfavorable current of perhaps more than 6 miles per hour. You can see that forecasting the tides is not just an intellectual exercise but a matter of great practical importance. Because of the hopelessness of predicting the tides from theory, oceanographers have resorted to forecasts based on observations. The water levels at various stations throughout the world, usually near ports, are measured at the same times each day for long periods. Meteorological changes average themselves out. The methods of harmonic analysis are applied to these records, and the result is a tidal table which predicts the times and heights of high and low water at each of these stations.

Tidal Friction

As the earth rotates on its axis its tidal bulge is held in place by the moon (neglecting the effect of the sun). The solid earth turns underneath the hump of the tide, and because of friction between the two tries to drag this bulge along with it. The contest between earth and moon is resolved as Figure 8–3 shows. The bulge is pulled ahead of the expected position by the rotation of the earth. What are the results of this tidal friction?

Not only is the earth dragging the bulge forward, the bulge is also pulling back on the earth, preventing it from rotating as fast as before. Because of tidal friction, in other words, *the earth slows down.* If the earth turns more slowly, this must mean that the day is grow-

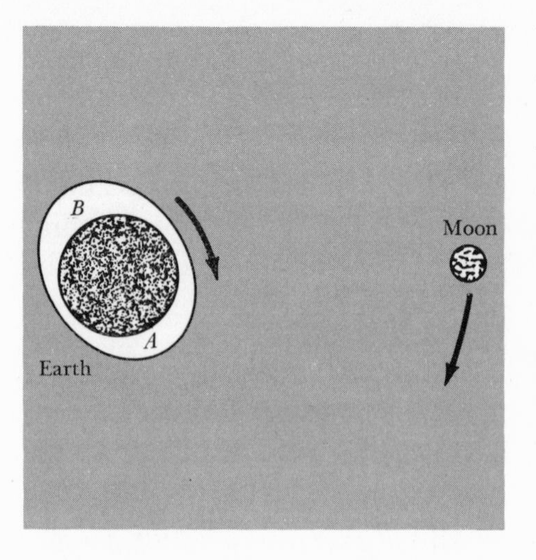

Figure 8–3. The solid earth turns beneath the hump of the tide and, because of friction between the two, drags the bulge ahead of the imaginary line between the earth's and moon's centers. This tidal friction slows the earth and results in a longer day.

ing longer! Confirmation of this amazing hypothesis is found in old records. The day is indeed growing gradually longer, but at a very slow rate. The change in the length of the day over the last one hundred years is about 1/1000 second. This is a small but not negligible amount, especially when you consider the cumulative effect over the centuries. The universal plea for "more hours in the day" is thus being answered, although too slowly to do us any good.

Another consequence of tidal friction is that the moon's orbital speed v is increased. This happens because the bulge at A, moving ahead of the moon, pulls the moon along with it. If v increases, then the gravitational attraction of the earth for the moon is no longer sufficient to hold the moon in the same orbit. What happens is that the radius of the orbit r increases also until a new balance is reached. An increasing value for r means that the moon is gradually drawing away from the earth—again, not very fast. Each century the moon moves about five feet farther away, not very much except over a long term. What can we expect over a period of many years? One scientist estimates that in fifty billion years the moon will rotate as fast as the earth. Before this time the moon will be so far away that solar tides will be more important than lunar ones. The day will be longer than the month. All this may come to pass simply because the oceans can be drawn up into tides.

Tides in the Earth and the Atmosphere

Although the earth resists being deformed, there are small tidal distortions in its solid body. These are associated with changes in *g*, the acceleration of gravity, so gravimeters are used to detect the earth tide. The bulging out of the earth amounts to at most about one foot at "high tide." Luckily for our sense of balance this transition takes place gradually over a period of twelve hours so that our feet are raised an inch an hour on the average, and we are not aware of the change.

Even the atmosphere surrounding the earth experiences a tide which is shown up by a daily fluctuation in barometric pressure.

Now that we have finished investigating the interaction of the moon and sun on the bulge they raise on earth, we shall look at their effect on a different sort of earth bulge. This is the phenomenon called *precession.*

Precession

When you first see a demonstration of precession it looks like magic—a miracle. You wait expectantly for the explanation of what you have seen—and the chances are you get no explanation. Many phenomena in physics can be explained, or at least made plausible, with the help of a picture and perhaps a little bit of algebra. On the other hand, there are many others that can be accounted for only with the help of mathematics, and usually mathematics beyond the algebra to which we are limiting this book. There is no simple diagram that will make such phenomena seem suddenly obvious. Unfortunately precession belongs to this class, so we shall simply describe it. Please do not think, however, that supernatural forces must intervene to produce precession!

We start with two spinning tops. You see from Figure 8–4a that the first top is rather unusual; it is a disk on an axle. At first we hold the top while one end of the axle rests on the support; then we set it spinning very fast and let go. What happens? I am sure that you, like me, expected the top to fall to the table. But, no, it stays there, lying horizontally in the air as we left it.

Figure 8–4. Precession. In figure (a) the disk is supported by a hand and then set spinning. Figure (b) shows the motion performed by the disk. Instead of falling, the end of the axle attached to the disk describes a horizontal circle around the support. Figure (c) is a top view of this motion.

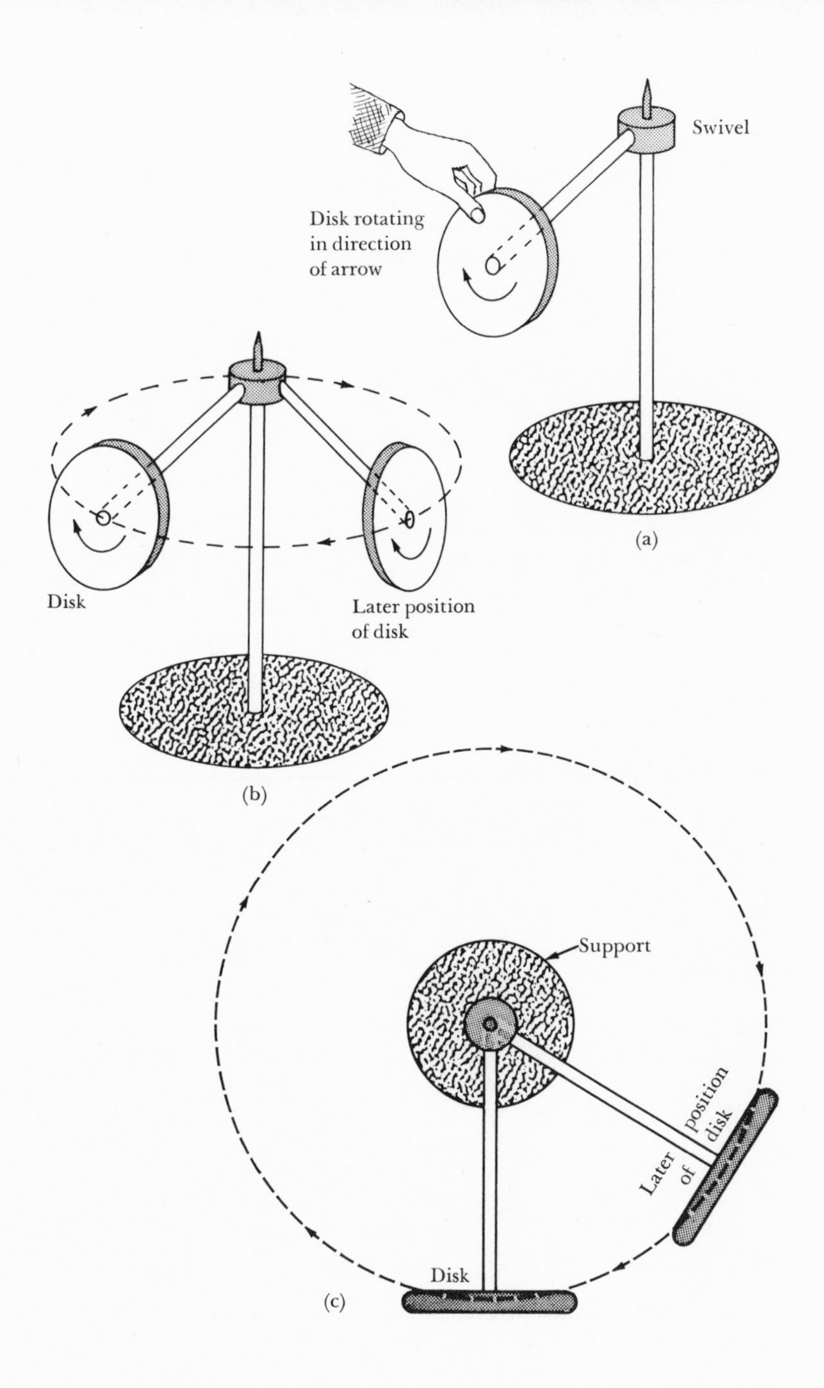
Swivel
Disk rotating
in direction
of arrow
(a)
Disk
Later position
of disk
(b)
Support
Later
position
of
disk
Disk
(c)

It *is*, however, moving. The free end of the axle is tracing a circle around the support, as you see in Figure 8–4b, in a rotation called *precession*. You probably recognize this device as a simple toy *gyroscope*. The behavior of this top goes against everything we expect from common sense and from what we know of physics as well. Here we have a force, gravity, applied downward on the top, and instead of falling, it moves slowly *sideways* to describe a circle! Very odd!

Figure 8–5. A top spinning fast enough will not fall down despite the torque exerted by its weight *mg*. Instead it will precess, that is it will remain at the same angle with a vertical axis while its axis of rotation describes a circle, as shown, about this vertical axis, and the foot of the top stays in place.

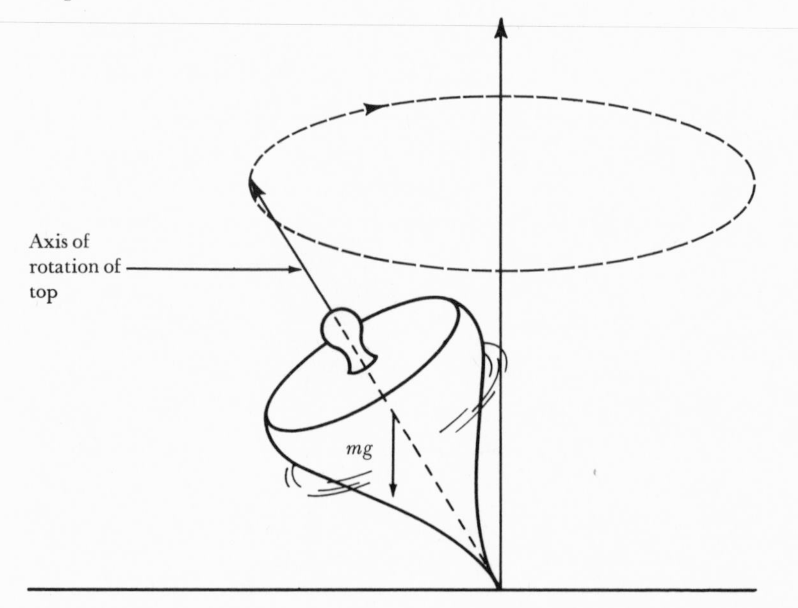

The next top we look at is the traditional type shown in Figure 8–5. As long as the top is spinning fast enough it stands up, spinning away until friction slows it down and it falls to the floor. While it spins it precesses, that is, the knob on its handle turns slowly about a vertical axis, while the foot of the top stays in place. Because you have seen this sort of top since you were two years old its behavior seems less extraordinary than that of the first, but really the two situations are the same. The top is tilted; it should fall down, but *as long as it keeps on spinning fast* it seems to defy gravity and stay up.

Torque

What do these tops have in common? First, they do not fall even though a gravitational force is acting on them—but they do move in another direction. Secondly, they are acted upon not only by a force, but also by something called a *torque.* Torque, sometimes called moment, is defined as the product of a force on a body times the distance from where the force acts to some turning point. Torque implies turning, therefore there must be some turning point, or line, about which torques are calculated. This becomes clear if you look at the diagram of Figure 8–6. The simplest case is in Figure 8–6a, where the force acts perpendicularly to the rod; the torque about the point of support O is Fd. In Figure 8–6b the force acts at an angle θ to the rod, so we must take its component perpendicular to the rod, $F \sin\theta$, to find the torque about O, which is $Fd \sin\theta$. In the seesaw in Figure 8–6c

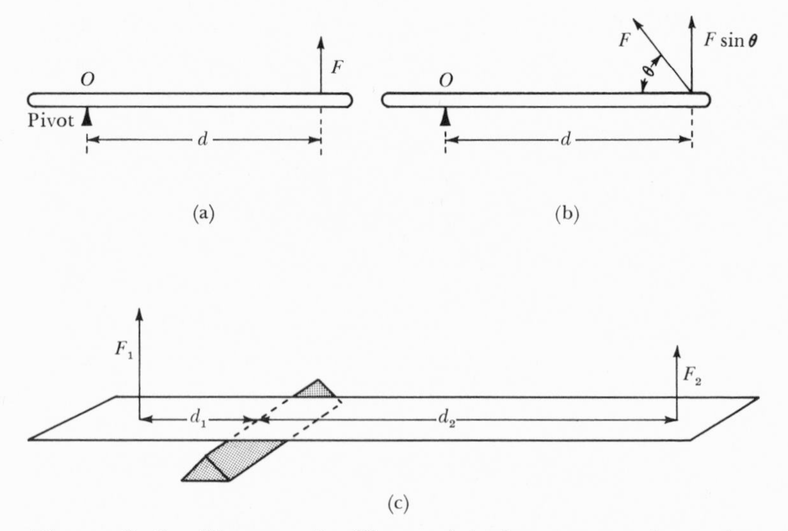

Figure 8–6. Torque. In Figure (a) the torque about the pivot point is *Fd.* In Figure (b) the torque is $Fd \sin\theta$, where $Fd \sin\theta$ is the component of F perpendicular to the rod. The seesaw in Figure (c) is balanced, which implies that the torque of F_2 about the pivot must be equal to the torque of F_1 about that pivot, or, in other words, $F_1d_1 = F_2d_2$. Notice that in (a) and (b) the rod is so thin that we can consider the torque about a *point,* but in the case of the seesaw the torque is about an *axis,* the line on which the seesaw is balanced.

there are two torques about the support. The seesaw is balanced with no tendency to turn, so the two torques must be equal: $F_1d_1 = F_2d_2$. Perhaps you recognize this as the balance or lever equation.

Torque is analogous to force. Whereas forces produce accelerations, or rates of change of velocity, torques produce rates of change of *angular velocity.* (Angular velocity can be expressed in revolutions per second.) If we inspect the rod in Figure 8–6a or b after *F* begins to act, we find it turning faster and faster about *O*.

The earth itself is a huge top and will precess if a torque is applied to it. You know that the earth is spinning, but where does the torque come from? We find this answer from the shape of the earth.

The Equatorial Bulge

The earth is not a perfect sphere but, even forgetting the slight hump raised as the tide, has a bulge around its middle which comes from centrifugal reaction force. (A good excuse to remember if you happen to have a bulge around *your* middle.) Unlike the tidal bulge, this deformation does not change its location throughout the day but is uniform around the earth. Figure 8–7 shows this bulge shaded and exaggerated.

How can centrifugal force produce this bulge? To answer this we imagine the earth sliced as an onion

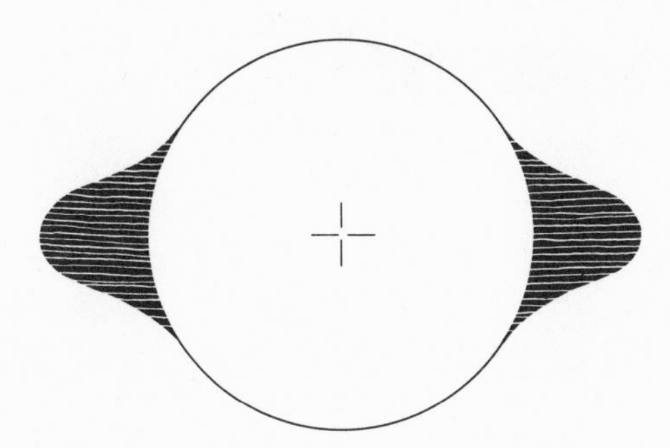

Figure 8–7. A cross section through the earth showing, shaded and exaggerated, its bulge caused by centrifugal force.

would be to make fried onion rings. Figure 8–8 shows two of these slices and several rings. Let us ask what the centrifugal force is in various rings. The equation as given on page 67, $F = mv^2/r$, is in an awkward form for us to use, as it depends on the orbital velocity v, which changes from ring to ring. We would prefer an expression that depends on a number that is constant over the entire earth. Such a number is the angular

Figure 8–8. The earth divided into rings to illustrate that equatorial slices experience more centrifugal reaction force than do slices near the poles.

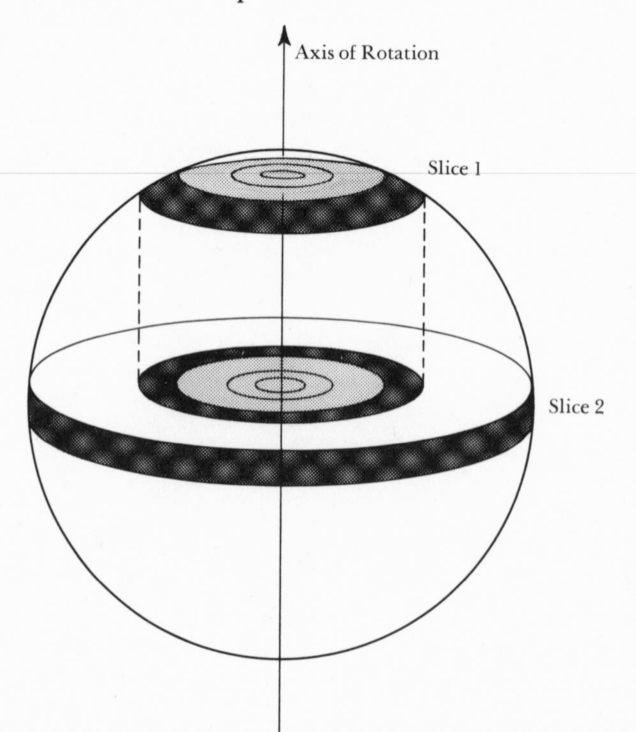

velocity ω which, divided by 2π, is the number of revolutions per second, its speed of rotation. The equation for centrifugal force in terms of ω is $F = m\omega^2 r$. From this form of the equation it is obvious that there is a greater centrifugal force acting on the rings of larger r (those farthest from the center) than on those of smaller r, which are near the axis of rotation. The outer ring of the equatorial slice in Figure 8–8 will feel more force than the inner rings on this slice, or than any of the rings in slice 1. The contributions to the centrifugal force on slice 2 (the equatorial slice) are made up of the forces acting on the rings inside the black ring and those outside it. You can see that slice 2 will be acted upon by a greater force than will slice 1 and in general that there is more bulging-out force acting on the slices nearest the equator than on those farthest away. The radius of the earth at the equator is thirteen miles greater than it is at the poles as a result.

The Precession of the Earth

It is the equatorial bulge which gives the sun and the moon a "handle" on which to exert a torque about the earth's center. This torque also depends on the accident that the plane of the earth's equator happens to be tilted at an angle of 23½° to the plane of its orbit about the sun, and at about the same angle to the moon's orbit. The gravitational force of the sun and the moon on the spherical part of the earth acts

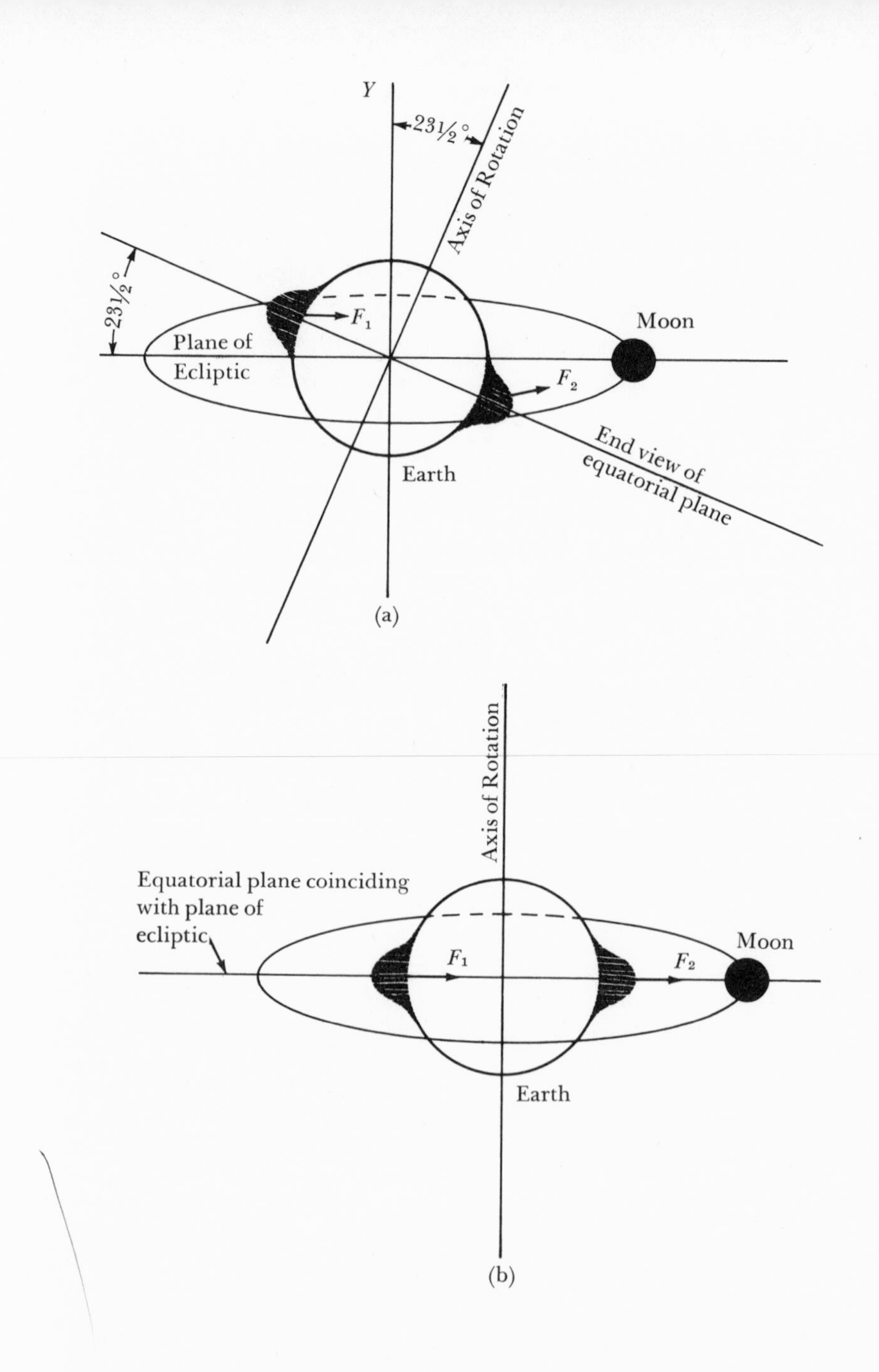
Y
23½°
Axis of Rotation
23½°
F_1
Moon
Plane of
Ecliptic
F_2
End view of
equatorial plane
Earth
(a)
Axis of Rotation
Equatorial plane coinciding
with plane of
ecliptic
F_1
F_2
Moon
Earth
(b)

as though it is concentrated in the center of the earth and so it cannot produce any torque about this center. On the other hand, the sun and the moon are attracted to the different parts of the bulge as to separate bodies. The bulge that is farther away from the sun or the moon feels less force than the other. The result is a net torque about the center of the earth, as you can see quite clearly from Figure 8–9a. You can also see from this diagram that if the earth were not tilted, but instead appeared as in Figure 8–9b, the forces

Figure 8–9. The torques exerted by the moon and the sun on the earth's bulges. For simplicity the moon alone is shown. Figure (a) shows (not to scale) the earth's equatorial plane tilted at 23½° to the plane of the ecliptic, that is, the plane in which the moon performs its orbit about the earth, and in which the earth orbits the sun. As the axis of rotation is perpendicular to the equatorial plane it follows that this axis is at an angle of 23½° to the vertical axis which is perpendicular to the plane of the ecliptic.

The force F_1 tends to turn the axis of rotation clockwise about the center while the force F_2, which is larger, produces a counterclockwise torque. The result is a net counterclockwise torque which would tend to reduce the tilt of the axis of rotation. As the earth is spinning, however, instead of moving more nearly upright it precesses as shown in Figure 8–10.

Figure (b) shows that if the earth were not tipped with respect to the plane of the ecliptic, the moon (and sun) could not produce a torque about the center since the forces acting on the bulges would in this case go *through* the center.

from the sun and the moon would pass through the center of the earth and there would be no torque about the center.

If the earth were not spinning, the torque would twist the earth's axis toward a position along the vertical axis labeled *Y* in Figures 8–9 and 8–10, the line per-

Figure 8–10. The precession of the earth. The tip of the axis of rotation of the earth describes a circle about the vertical axis *Y* while the axis itself describes a cone in space whose angle is 47°. The period of precession is 26,000 years.

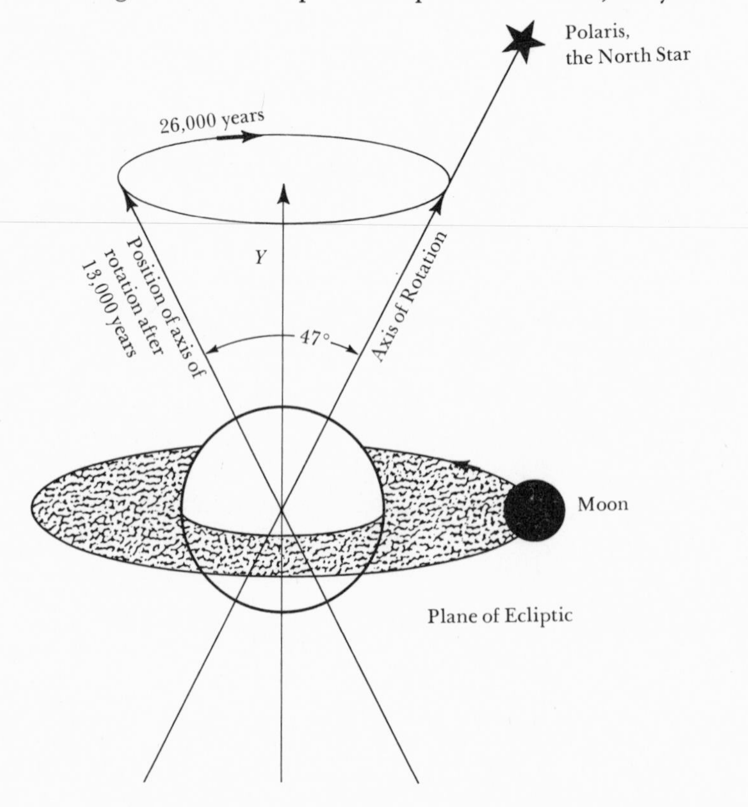

pendicular to the plane of the ecliptic. In other words, the effect of the torque would be to decrease the tilt of the earth's axis. Because the earth is rotating on its axis, however, it must behave like any other top. Its angle of tilt remains the same at 23½°, but the axis of rotation precesses about the vertical line *Y* as shown in Figure 8–10. As it precesses, the earth's axis draws a cone in space, a cone whose angle is 47° and which takes about 26,000 years to complete. This rate of precession may not be very great, but it is noticeable. Our North Pole, the northern tip of our axis of rotation, points to Polaris, the North Star. Five thousand years ago, at the time of the Egyptian Pharaohs, the North Pole pointed to another star, Alpha Draconis. In the year 14,000 the bright star Vega will be close enough to the Pole to be the "north star" for navigators, if indeed there are still people who navigate by the stars in that year.

Precession was first noticed by the change in position of the equinoxes, the points at which the sun's orbit cuts the earth's equatorial plane. There are two equinoxes: the vernal equinox which announces the beginning of spring on about March 21, and the autumnal equinox which ushers in fall near September 21. Hipparchus observed the changes in position of the equinox as early as 125 B.C., but the precession could not be explained until Newton solved the problem by applying his own law of gravitation to it.

chapter nine

EARTH SATELLITES

Until October 4, 1957, the earth had only one satellite, the moon. On that historic day Russian scientists performed the remarkable feat of sending a man-made object out past the earth's atmosphere and into an orbit around the earth. Despite our disappointment that scientists in the United States were not the first to achieve this wonderful deed, a stronger emotion was a pride that went beyond nationalism.

The Satellite Orbit

If we were to hurl a satellite into space by giving it one great push from a launching pad on the earth, we would have to send it off with an initial velocity of 18,000 miles per hour. We get this number very simply by balancing the satellite weight mg against the centrifugal reaction force mv^2/r, which yields the orbital velocity $v = \sqrt{rg}$. By substituting the values of 6.4×10^6 meters for the radius of the earth r and 9.8 meters per second per second for g, we get a value for v of 7.9×10^3 meters per second or 18,000 miles per hour. This figure is the minimum velocity that a satellite must have in order to orbit the earth *near the earth;* with less speed than this the rocket will fall to earth like an ordinary projectile.

In practice the satellite never receives the speed it needs for a given orbit all at once on the launching pad. Instead the satellite is carried to the desired height by a rocket. This rocket must fight its way through a barrier of atmospheric friction as well as gravity. Friction increases rapidly with speed, so it is obviously better for the rocket to go slowly until it is outside the lower and denser parts of the atmosphere. The rocket picks up speed from its own engines, which allows it to start slowly and accelerate to the required speed. The gradual start also benefits the instruments carried by the rocket and satellite as well as any humans who might be aboard the spaceship. When the rocket reaches the desired height it must be turned so that the satellite moves parallel to the earth and, given the correct speed, the rocket then falls away. Having performed its task, it is needed no longer. If the satellite is sent off toward the east along the equator, it gets a free gift of 1,000 miles per hour added to its speed, the speed of rotation of the earth. At the poles the rocket would get no benefit from this rotation, while at intermediate points the amount of the boost depends on the latitude.

The Right Speed for the Orbit

A satellite in a distant orbit will go slower than one in an orbit closer to the earth. This is because the gravitational force on the spaceship decreases the farther away it is from the earth. The table opposite shows the relationship between height of the orbit above the earth and the orbital velocity needed at that height. The speed of the first entry in that table is 25,900 feet per second, which is equivalent to 18,000 miles per hour, the number we gave earlier. The height of "zero feet" really means any height low enough so the *g* can be considered equal to 32 feet per second per second. In any case, the number is only theoretical as no one is likely to put a satellite into orbit a few feet above our heads.

Minimum Height for the Orbit

The density of the atmosphere grows less and less with altitude. At a height of one hundred miles above the earth the density is about one thousand millionth what it is at the surface. Even so, the orbit of a satellite at that height is affected by atmospheric friction, whereas at two hundred miles it would feel essentially no drag. Because satellite orbits are elliptical, when the satellite passes near the earth it may go through the atmosphere, as in Figure 9–1. Part of the rocket engineer's problem consists of keeping the satellite outside the atmosphere, which changes the size and shape of its orbit and reduces its lifetime. For a lifetime in orbit of more than two weeks the satellite should not be any closer than 110 miles to the earth.

EFFECT OF ORBIT DISTANCE ON VELOCITY AND PERIOD OF CIRCULAR ORBIT

Distance from Earth (miles)	*Orbital Velocity (feet per second)*	*Period (minutes)*	*(days)*
0	25,900	84.5	
100	25,600	88	
400	24,700	98	
1,000	23,100	118	
22,000	10,060	approximately	1
230,000	3,360		27

Figure 9–1. A satellite orbit may pass through the earth's atmosphere, subjecting the satellite to atmospheric friction.

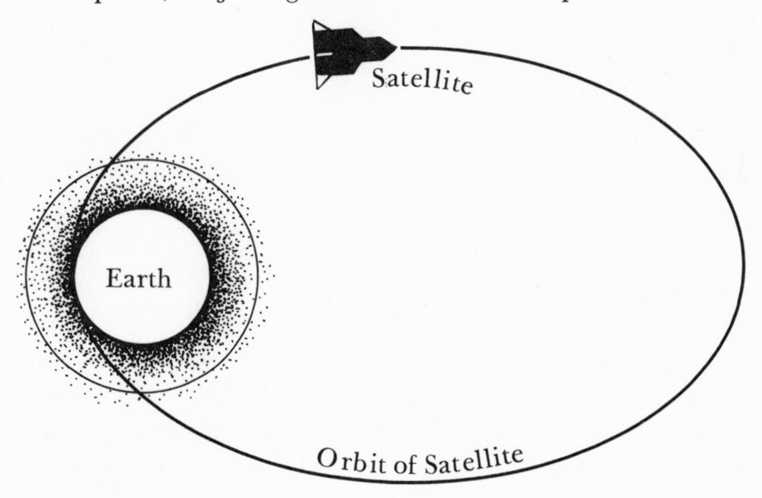

At this time (mid-1968) it is reported that the communications satellite Echo I, launched in August, 1960, is about to die. This was the first satellite to be visible to the naked eye. An aluminized plastic bag, it caught the light from the sun long after it had set on earth. It moved through the early evening sky like a swift star, a bright advertisement for man's accomplishment. It will be sad to see it go.

Precession

The same equatorial bulges that make the earth precess also cause the plane of the satellite's orbit to precess about the earth. The orbit gradually swings backward at a rate of about 2° of longitude a day. If the satellite could somehow trace a visible line in space, like an airplane's vapor trail, it would look like Figure 9–2. Because the precession depends on the amount of the bulging of the earth, scientists have turned this fact around and used the observations of precession to give a precise measurement of the extent of bulging.

Satellite Periods

Notice from the table on page 139, not only do satellites in different orbits travel with different velocities, but they also have different periods. The periods grow larger as orbit distance increases. Sputnik I, the first satellite, went around the earth in

Figure 9–2. The equatorial bulges of the earth cause the plane of the satellite's orbit to precess about the earth.

about 1½ hours. However, this does not mean that Sputnik passed over your head every hour and one half because, do not forget, you too are moving. As the earth turns on its axis it carries you around with it at the not inconsiderable speed of 1,000 miles per hour (at the equator)! While the Sputnik was whizzing around the earth you were not standing still waiting for it. When the spaceship came back to its starting point, you were already about 1,500 miles away if you were at the equator, and the Sputnik had to catch up. There *is* an orbit, however, whose speed is such that the satellite goes around the earth in 24 hours. To someone underneath, the satellite seems stopped overhead because the person and the spaceship are going around at the same speed. This so-called stationary orbit occurs at an altitude of a little over 22,000 miles.

Escaping Gravity

The satellites we have been describing are bound to the earth, destined to move in orbits around it until they "die." It is a much greater feat for a spaceship to escape the earth entirely, to get far enough away so that it is not trapped in the gravitational field of the earth. To survey Venus, to embark on any of the amazing voyages to other parts of the solar system that are proposed by scientists, the space probe must leave the world behind and go off on its own. And to reach the moon the spaceship must already have gone beyond most of the earth's gravity.

By using calculus and knowing how g changes with

distance from the earth, it is easy to calculate the velocity a body needs to escape completely from the earth—in other words, to go from the earth's surface to an infinite distance where the gravitational attraction has finally diminished to zero. In practice this is the same velocity that the body needs to get far enough away so that gravity is negligible. This so-called *escape velocity* turns out to be

$$v_{\text{escape}} = \sqrt{2\,gr} = 11{,}200 \text{ meters per second (for the earth)}$$
$$= \text{about } 25{,}000 \text{ miles per hour.}$$

The letter r stands for the radius of the earth, 6.38×10^6 meters.

On January 2, 1959, the Russian Lunik did reach a velocity greater than the escape velocity. It passed within three thousand miles of the moon and then went beyond to be trapped in the sun's gravitational field and become the first artificial planet. An earlier effort, the American Pioneer I, was meant to go into an orbit around the moon, to become, if you like, a moon's moon. Unfortunately the rocket of this first of the Pioneer series burned out a few moments too soon and the Pioneer I never made it to the region of the moon.

To orbit the moon the rocket must be aimed just right to meet the moon not where it *is* at the launching time but where it *will be* when the rocket reaches the moon's orbit. See Figure 9–3. The probe must be equipped with *retro-rockets* which fire backward and slow the rocket down by exactly the right amount so that it can go into orbit around the moon. Getting a

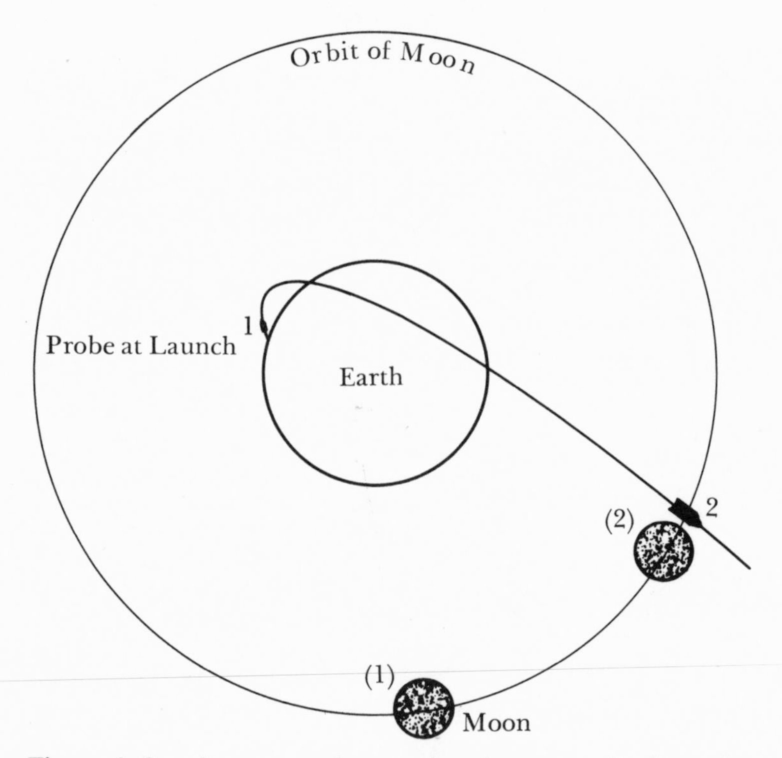

Figure 9–3. A moon probe meeting the moon. As the probe is launched 1 the moon is at position (1). The probe must be launched in such a way that when the moon is at position (2) the probe will be there too.

rocket to the moon is not an easy problem to solve, yet today it has become commonplace to read in the newspapers of probes actually landing on the moon, of American lunar probes touching the moon so gently that they are able to send photographs of the moon's surface back to earth. What ten years ago would have been science fiction is accepted casually today, the idea that teams of astronauts are training to land on the moon in the near future. When astronauts can steer their spaceship so close to another that they can "dock" with it, as they did in Project Gemini, when a man can leave his ship to "walk" in space, when probes can land on the moon itself, it is not hard to believe that man will indeed soon set foot on the moon.

Rocket Trips to the Planets

The moon is not the astronauts' only target. Venus has already been examined by spaceships, and travel to the planets is a possibility. The limitation is time. Some stars are too far away for us ever to hope to visit them. Venus and Mars are each about fifty million miles from the earth at their nearest point of approach; if the rocket has too little speed left after leaving the earth's field, the trip will be too long for human passengers. One problem, for example, is food. A long voyage means that much food has to be carried by the rocket, and that adds to the load. Let us imagine that the passage to Venus is to take a year, longer perhaps than most people could support. A two-year supply of food would have to be loaded onto the ship. It would have to travel at a speed of about 5,708 miles per hour, the extra speed over the escape velocity, to arrive in a year's time.

When the space probe finally enters the gravity-free region no force is needed to keep it moving. A spaceship beyond gravity and the atmosphere is a very pure illustration of Newton's First Law. No forces act on the ship, and so it continues to move at whatever speed it has left over from the 25,000 miles per hour escape velocity. The only forces that need to be applied are to change its direction, and this can be accomplished with very lightweight engines.

Weightlessness

Because our bodies have evolved in an environment in which gravity is present they cannot easily cope with a gravity-free existence. When a spaceship is in orbit the force of gravity acting on it is balanced by the centrifugal reaction force of its orbital motion. The passengers within may feel very uncomfortable in this absence of gravity, and if their voyage is a long one their bodies may show ill effects. Anything not tied down in the cabin of the spaceship moves hither and thither with no force to keep it down, or even up. Not only is this annoying; it can be quite dangerous if, for example, a bit of floating debris such as solder or a screw should land where it can cause trouble. Moving around the cabin is difficult. Walking on earth depends on friction, which in turn depends on gravity. "Walking" without gravity is like skating on the smoothest of skating rinks. There is nothing for your foot to push against. You weigh actually nothing, since weight equals mg, but you look just as fat or thin as before. A spaceship that has left the earth and its gravity field faces the same problem of weightlessness. A few not-very-well-publicized reports suggest that the Russian and the United States' astronauts who were aloft for long periods suffered physical ill effects which lasted after the flights. Plant seeds, on the other hand, respond remarkably well to gravity-free flight, growing much faster than on earth. Much more experience in long gravity-free flights is needed before we can be sure of their effects on the human body.

It does seem clear, however, that for long flights some sort of artificial gravity must be provided. One system has already been mentioned in this book. In this method the spaceship is spun about an axis so that a centrifugal force is produced which mimics gravity. This kind of "gravity" would take a while to get accustomed to because, for instance, the "gravity" would change from point to point in the cabin. On the other hand, the spinning would provide an "up" and a "down" and might make life in space a little easier than it otherwise would be. No manned spaceship has yet used a system of artificial gravity.

The Rocket Engine

Because this is a book on gravity and not on space travel, we must not get too deeply involved in the very interesting technology of rocketry. On the other hand, you should at least understand a little about the operation of the rocket engine. A rocket works by burning fuel that produces hot gases which are ejected at high speed from behind. Many people think incorrectly that the rocket goes up because the gases push against the launching pad and then against the air. This is not true at all. The rocket does not work by pushing, and in fact it works best in space where there is nothing to push against. The principle behind its operation is called the *conservation of momentum.* This states that when no *external* forces act on a system a quantity known as *momentum* is unchanged. Momentum is defined as the product of the mass m of a body or of a system and its velocity v, or the vector sum of the velocities of a system. Momentum $= mv$. In this case the system consists of the rocket and the gases. See Figure 9–4. The original momentum when the rocket is at rest on its pad is zero, so it must remain zero. When the hot gases rush out their downward momentum is great, because even though the mass of the gases is small their speed is very high. This downward momentum must be balanced by an upward motion of the rocket; because it is so much heavier than the gases the rocket moves much more slowly than the gases, but it does rise, and continues to do so as long as the engine operates. The rocket recoils upward as a result of shooting off high-speed gas.

Multistage Rockets

It is technologically impossible at this point to build a single rocket that can achieve final speeds great enough to put it into orbit around the earth, let alone to escape the earth. The problem is that to reach high speeds the rocket must carry a heavy load of fuel, which makes a greater load to be accelerated by the rocket engine. To reach the first bound orbit a rocket must carry a weight of fuel about thirty-seven times the weight of the entire remainder of the rocket

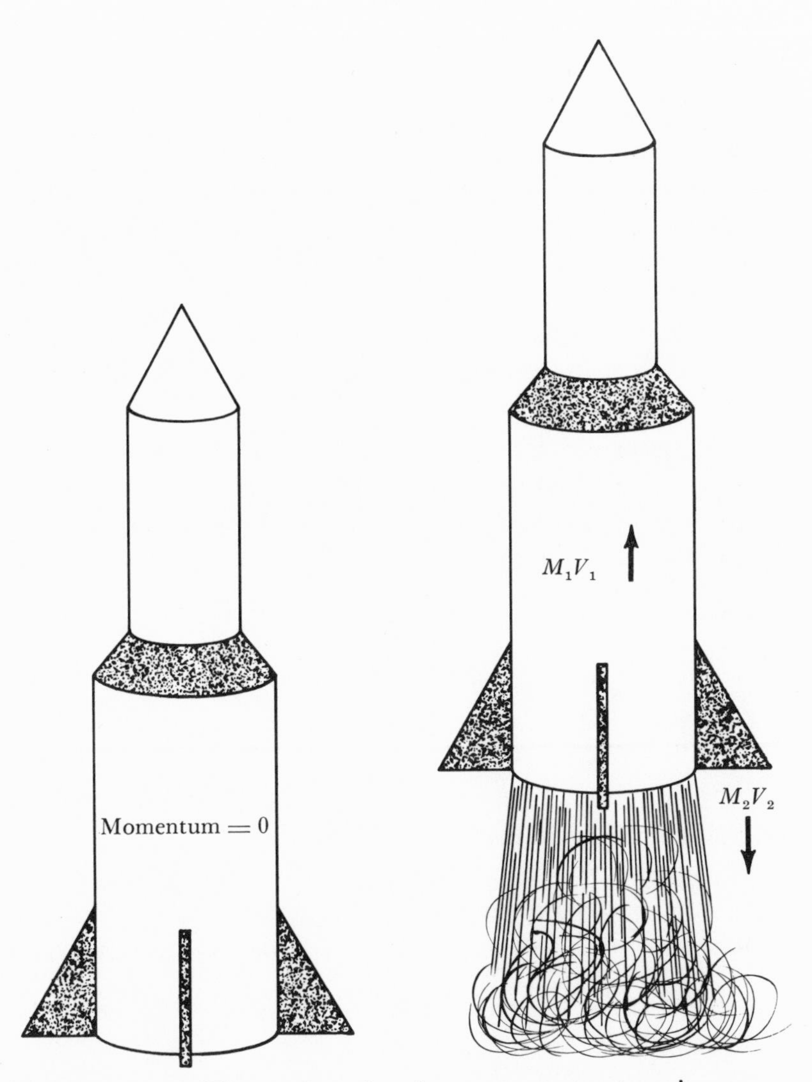

Figure 9–4. The rocket rises because momentum is conserved. In the first figure the momentum M_1V_1 of the rocket is zero. In the second picture the momentum of the system must remain the same, as zero. Since the hot gases have the momentum M_2V_2 downward this must be balanced by an upward momentum of the rocket $M_1V_1 = M_2V_2$.

assembly, including the satellite, the instruments, and of course the fuel tanks! This difficulty was circumvented by the ingenious solution of using more than one rocket to boost the load into space. The rockets fire one after the other as succeeding rockets burn out. Figure 9–5 shows the operation of the multistage rocket. As the first rocket, or the first stage, burns out it falls away, reducing the load by its weight. The rest of the rocket continues to rise because the second stage now fires, carrying the reduced load higher until it too is spent and it too falls away. By building up a rocket like this we could achieve almost unlimited speeds. As it is, three stages are a practical compromise, and this allows the rocket to reach escape velocity and more.

Debris in Space

The number of spaceships that have been launched is more than three hundred and is increasing all the time. Some of them have simply burned up on reentering our atmosphere at high speed, but most are still in space. Add to this number the support-

Figure 9–5. A three-stage rocket. In (a) the entire rocket lifts from the ground. When the fuel in the first stage is spent it falls to the ground, leaving the second stage to carry the rocket farther, (b). When the fuel of the second stage is used up it too falls away, and the third and last stage fires to carry on, (c).

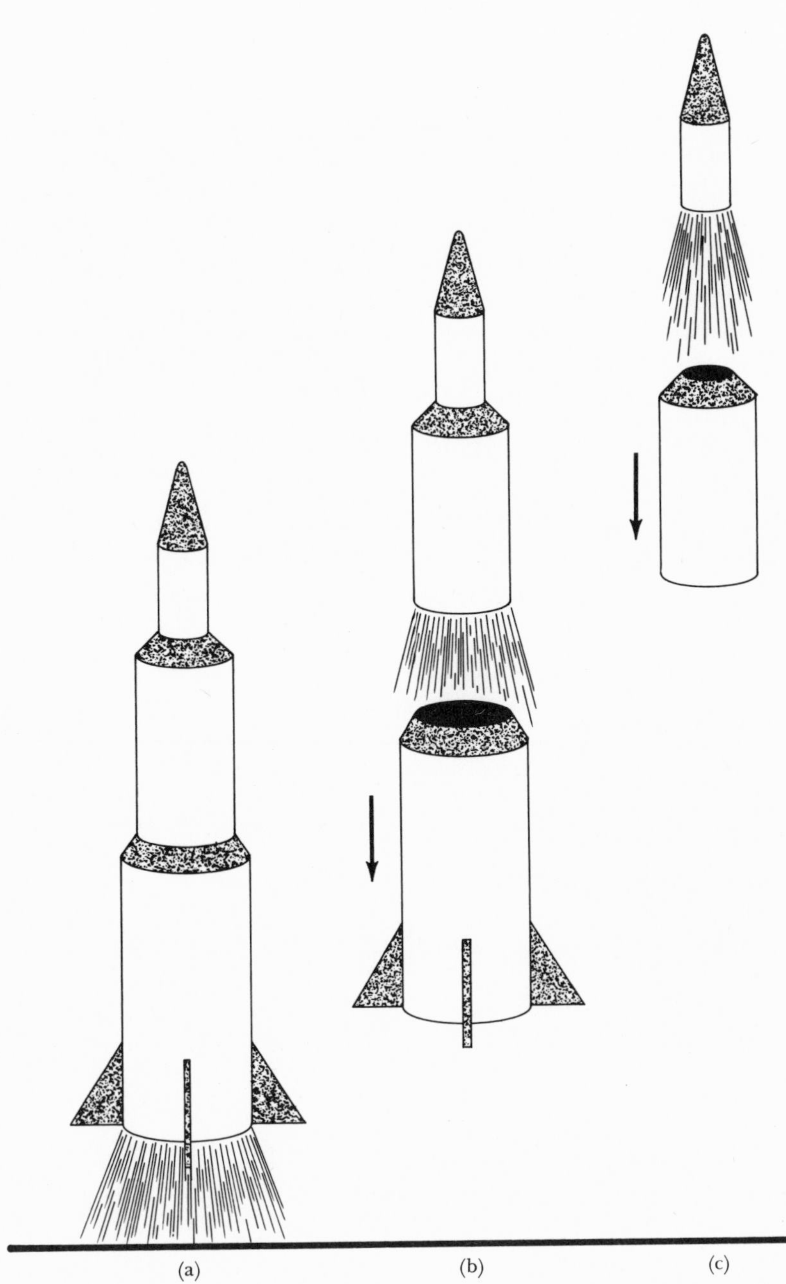
(a)
(b)
(c)

ing stages of the rockets, not all of which burned up, and other "junk" such as the umbilical cord used by the late Edward White for his "walk" in space and you can see "empty" space is becoming crowded with debris thrown into the skies by man. Perhaps the slogan for the twenty-first century will be "Keep Space Clean"!

Escape Velocity and the Atmosphere

Spaceships are not the only bodies that must reach a speed of 11,200 meters per second to escape from the earth's gravity; so must the molecules of the air. The earth keeps its atmosphere simply because the escape velocity is much higher than the average speed of the air molecules. The gas molecules that make up the air are, as you may know, in constant motion. This speed increases if the gas is heated, but at any particular temperature the average speed of the molecules of mass m of any one kind of gas depends on $1/\sqrt{m}$. In other words, the heavier the gas molecule the slower it will be moving. The lightest gas of all is hydrogen, whose molecules have therefore the highest average speed, about 2,000 meters per second. This speed is not great enough to allow the average molecule to escape from the earth. Not all the molecules are moving with the average speed, however; in fact there is a great spread of velocities on either side of the average. Many molecules of hydrogen and of the next lightest gas, helium, have speeds in excess of the escape velocity

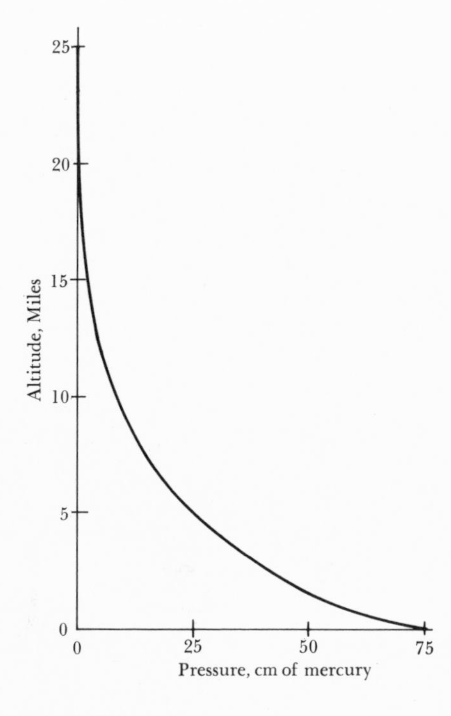

Figure 9–6. A graph of atmospheric pressure versus altitude at latitude 45°.

and so these molecules left the atmosphere permanently long ago. The result is that helium and hydrogen, while very common elsewhere in the universe, are rare in the earth's atmosphere. Gases whose molecules are heavier, such as oxygen and nitrogen, have fewer molecules that achieve escape velocity and therefore they are retained by the earth to make up the greater part of the atmosphere. The escape velocity from the moon is only about 2,400 meters per second, and it is unable to hold an atmosphere.

It is because of gravity that the atmospheric pressure decreases with altitude in the manner shown in Figure 9–6. The number of molecules at a given height depends in a complicated way on this height. This equation takes into account the fact that only those molecules with high speeds will reach high altitudes against gravity, and it uses the known distribution of speeds among the molecules. The density and therefore the pressure at a given height depend on the number of molecules at that height, but we need not reproduce the complicated formula that gives pressure in terms of height. The situation is much easier to understand from the graph in Figure 9–6. Pressure goes down as height increases.

chapter ten GRAVITY AND RELATIVITY

Although Newton formulated his law of gravity over three hundred years ago, and although we have been able to apply it in all the ways that have filled the preceding chapters, we certainly are not finished with the story of gravity. We don't even know what gravity is or just how it acts on a body at a distance. Does gravity travel as a wave like electromagnetic radiation? We don't know what to make of the tantalizing similarity between gravitational forces and electromagnetic forces, both of which depend on the inverse square of the distance between the interacting bodies.

Special Relativity

After Albert Einstein had formulated his theory of special relativity (1905), he began to ponder some of the problems of gravity. The result was his publication in 1916 of the general theory of relativity, which put forward some extraordinary ideas about gravity and which we will take up in this chapter. The special theory yielded the conclusion that the highest speed possible in the universe is the speed of light c. This upper limit is 3×10^8 meters per second in vacuum. The special theory was concerned with reference systems that were moving *at constant velocity* with respect to each other, for example, a train and the countryside it is passing. Another postulate of the special theory is that experiments performed in one reference system (the train, for instance) will give the same results as experiments performed in another system moving at a constant speed with respect to the first (the station). The laws of physics retain their form from one such system to another. Although the laws are unchanged, the dimensions in which they are expressed *are* changed. An object that has a length L along the direction of motion of a system moving with a speed v will appear to have a smaller length $L' = L\sqrt{1 - v^2/c^2}$ to an observer in a stationary system. And the reverse is also true.

Let us imagine the unlikely but (in principle) possible situation of a train flashing past a station at a speed of .44 times the speed of light c. The people on the train have measured and found that its length is 100 meters. An observer in the station finds that the length of the train is only $100\sqrt{1 - (.44c)^2/c^2} = 90$ meters. By a coincidence the station as measured by the stationmaster is also 100 meters long. The people on the train find that it is 90 meters long.

We had to exaggerate to illustrate the contraction of objects in the direction of motion. For bodies traveling at normal speeds, the ratio v^2/c^2 is so small as to be negligible and the observer would not be able to measure a contraction. But for bodies moving with speeds near the speed of light—elementary particles in the cosmic radiation or accelerated in the laboratory—this relativistic contraction becomes important. Not only is length affected by the relative motion; time is also. A clock moving with speed v past a stationary system will appear to be slow to observers in the stationary system. The interval between ticks of the moving clock appears greater to the stationary observer than to an observer moving with the clock, by the ratio $\sqrt{1 - v^2/c^2}$.

Principle of Equivalence

In the general theory of relativity Einstein attempted to express the laws of physics so that they could be transformed from one system to another that was *accelerated* with respect to the first. Although he was never completely successful in integrating electromagnetism and gravitation into a unified theory, the general theory makes some very interesting conclusions and predictions about gravity. The general theory of relativity is based on Einstein's *principle of equivalence.* This can be stated briefly: *An observer in a closed laboratory cannot tell the difference between effects caused by gravity and effects caused by an acceleration of the laboratory.* Now we shall see what this means.

We imagine a closed laboratory in a spaceship floating weightless in outer space. See Figure 10–1. There is an astronaut within who holds in each hand a ball, one of plastic and another the same size but made of lead. If he should let go the balls, they would stay

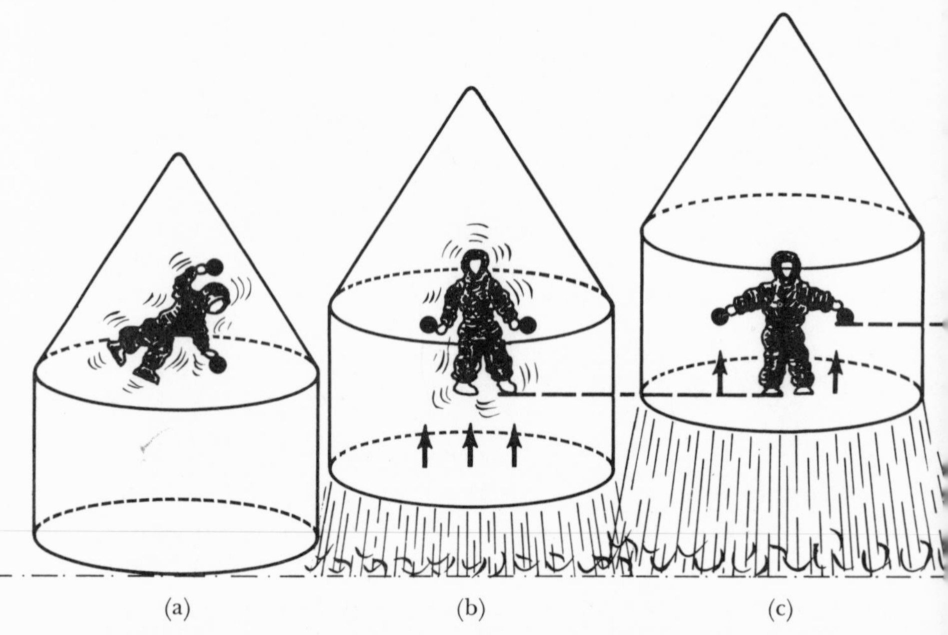

Figure 10–1. Einstein's principle of equivalence. (a) The spaceship is not accelerated and the astronaut is "floating." (b) The rocket fires and begins to accelerate, but the astronaut is not yet affected and remains in the same position *relative to us* while the floor of the spaceship moves up. (c) We see the astronaut still in the same position relative to us (dotted line) but the floor has met his feet. He believes he has fallen to the floor. A moment later he releases two balls of unequal weight and equal size. They acquire the velocity of the ship at the moment of release. (d) Because of their

where they were; no forces are acting on them. Suddenly, but without the astronaut's knowledge, the

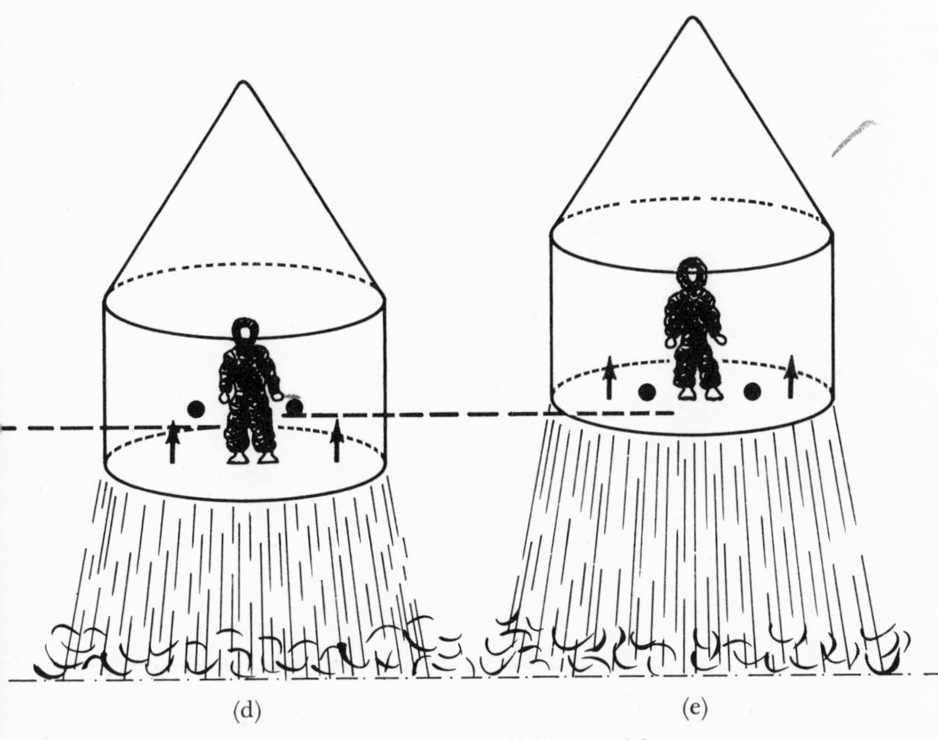

(d) (e)

velocity the balls move up (dotted line) with respect to us but at the same time the accelerated rocket moves up even more so that the balls are closer to the floor than in (c). The astronaut thinks they are falling. (e) Even though the balls have continued to move up (dotted line) the floor has caught up to them both at the same time. To the astronaut it appears that they have fallen to the floor, just as they would if gravity were acting upon them. It is not possible for him to distinguish between the effects of acceleration and the effects of gravity in this situation.

rocket fires and begins to accelerate at 32 feet per second per second. From our stationary observation point we (with Superman's X-ray vision, perhaps) see a curious sight. The man stays put relative to us while the floor of the cabin goes faster and faster upward until it hits his feet (or his head if he had been floating head down). He can stand normally and the furnishings of the cabin stay in place. If he now lets go the balls at the same time they will move upward, as we see it, at the speed that the rocket had when the astronaut released them. Meanwhile, because the rocket is accelerating, the floor goes faster and faster and soon catches up to the balls, meeting both simultaneously. This is our view of what happens; the astronaut sees the situation very differently. He believes that when he lets go the balls they drop, and as they hit the floor at the same time he concludes that he is somehow back on the surface of the earth with a gravitational force equal to that at the surface of the earth acting on him and his cabin. There is absolutely no way for him to tell whether he is in an accelerated laboratory or being affected by gravity. Even if the acceleration of the rocket were not 32 feet per second per second, he would still be confused because, after all, the acceleration of gravity is only equal to 32 feet per second per second near the surface of the earth; elsewhere it is different.

If the foregoing result were all that we could glean from the principle of equivalence, it would be interesting but trivial. You could be forgiven for saying, "So what?" But Einstein believed that the principle of equivalence applied not only to mechanical but also to electromagnetic phenomena, including light. To see why he could imagine that a supposedly massless manifestation like light could be affected by gravity, a really amazing idea, we have to go back a little bit in time.

Quanta

In 1900 the physicist Max Planck found that he could explain certain characteristics of black-body radiation (radiation produced by bodies hot enough to glow) if he imagined that this radiation was shot off in discrete bursts of energy called *quanta* instead of continuously. Planck was more disturbed than pleased at this solution, because he could not take seriously such a notion. James Clerk Maxwell had established the wave theory of light on very firm ground in the latter half of the nineteenth century, and from that time no one disputed that all the electromagnetic radiations—light waves, radio waves, X rays, and so on—were transmitted by a wave of the sort you see in Figure 10–2. Planck considered that his solution was a sort of mathematical trick without any physical validity. Another phenomenon that puzzled physicists at that time was known as the photoelectric effect. Albert Einstein realized that he could explain all the characteristics of the photoelectric effect if he took Planck's proposal seriously. From this beginning sprang the celebrated quantum theory which, developed into quantum mechanics, is the structure on which is built all of modern physics. Ironically Einstein never fully believed in the conclusions to which quantum mechanics pointed the way, while Planck remained appalled by the development of his original idea.

With the appearance of the quantum theory, physicists had a choice of two theories of light. One claimed that light, and all electromagnetic radiation, is emitted as continuous waves, like Figure 10–2, which continuously transfer the energy of the radiation. The other theory proposed that light energy is emitted in discrete bundles, the quanta. Is one theory correct while the other is false? The answer is that there really

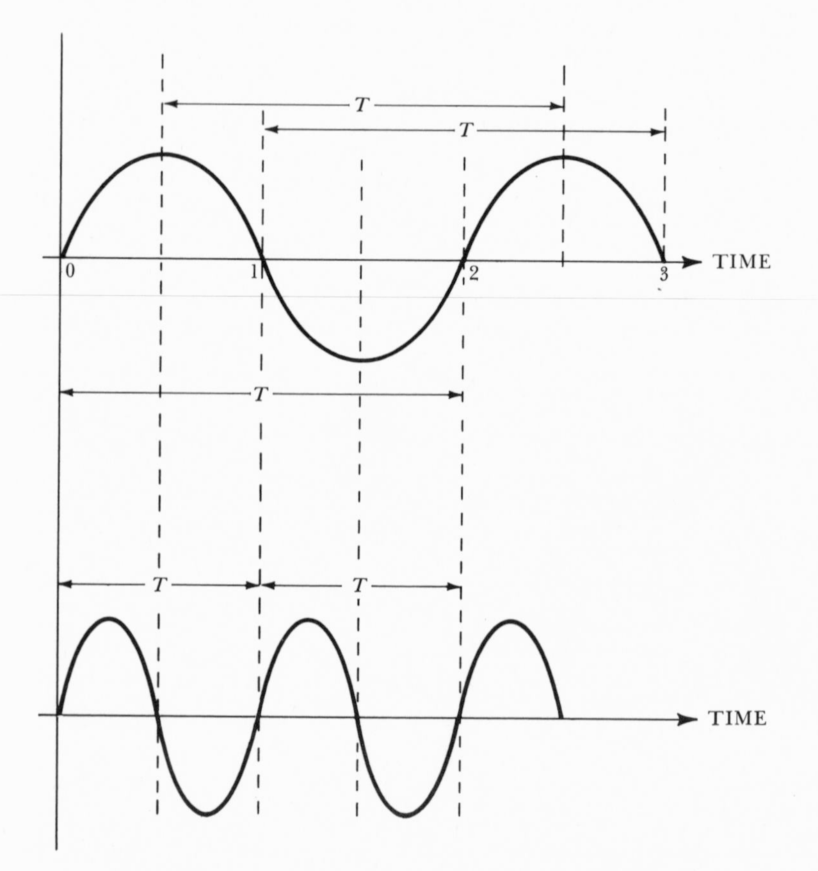

is no "choice" between theories; both are correct. The wave theory explains certain characteristics of light; the quantum theory explains others. Light has both a wave and a particle nature. In this discussion we are more interested in the particle side of light, in the traits of these particles associated with the quanta, the *photons.*

The Photon

Each photon carries one quantum of energy. We have been using the word "energy" loosely without defining it. The physicist calls energy the ability to do *work,* while "work" in the physicist's definition is the product of a force times the distance it moves. A body has the *kinetic energy* $mv^2/2$ if it is moving; or it may, like a body poised on the edge of a cliff, have *potential energy,* the possibility of doing work, which equals mgH, where H is the height of the cliff.

Figure 10–2. A wave. The interval of time needed for the wave to complete a *cycle,* that is, to return to its original height, is called the *period* T of the wave. As shown in the first drawing this period can be counted from any point on the wave to the time when the wave returns to this position, from origin to origin, or from maximum to maximum, or from minimum to minimum, for example. The maximum height which the wave reaches is called its *amplitude* and the number of cycles it performs per unit time (usually per second) is called its *frequency* f. You can see that as the second wave performs two cycles in the time that it takes the first wave to perform one cycle the frequency of the second wave is twice that of the first.

The potential energy can be converted to work when the body falls, as for example when water falls onto a mill wheel. There are other forms of energy as well. The size of a quantum of energy depends on the frequency f of the photon, with

$$E = hf$$

where h is known as Planck's constant.

"Frequency" is a property of all waves. During one *cycle* a wave rises to a maximum value, falls to zero, descends to a minimum below zero, and then returns to zero just as in Figure 10–2. The number of cycles it performs in a certain time is called the *frequency* of the wave. It is the frequency of a light wave that determines its color. The two opposite ends of the spectrum of visible light are blue light and red light, which have respectively the highest and lowest frequencies. It is odd to find that we can use a wave term like frequency to describe a photon, which is a particle. How can a particle have a frequency? We cannot give a simple answer to this question. It is the nature of quantum mechanics that its mathematical results do not correspond to a clear physical picture. We can say that the frequency of the photon is that of the wave which may also describe the same electromagnetic radiation.

The Mass of the Photon

One consequence of special relativity which we have not yet mentioned is the relativistic increase in mass. To a stationary observer a moving mass appears greater than its mass at rest by an amount $\sqrt{1 - v^2/c^2}$. For a lightweight particle which may attain high speeds this increase can be enormous—an electron moving with the not uncommon speed of .99 times the speed of light appears to have a mass *seven times* its "rest mass," the mass it would have at rest with respect to the observer. Using this expression, Einstein derived a startling result, the famous formula $E = mc^2$. If a body of mass m is completely destroyed, it becomes converted into an amount of energy equal to its mass times the speed of light squared! Mass and energy are entirely equivalent. This theory was vindicated with the explosion of the first atomic bomb in which matter was converted into an amount of energy unimaginable to those who were ignorant of the equivalence of mass and energy.

If mass is equivalent to energy, so is energy equivalent to mass. A photon, which has no rest mass, has, by virtue of its energy, a mass equal to E/c^2. Several paragraphs earlier we said that the energy of a photon is hf; this means that the mass of the photon is

$$m = \frac{hf}{c^2}.$$

As the photon has a mass associated with it, it, and therefore light, must be affected by gravity! Although this extraordinary conclusion is hard to swallow, we can go back to our imaginary rocket to see a situation in which this does after all seem reasonable.

The Bending of Light

We find the astronaut still in the rocket. It has become very dusty by now in the cabin so when he shines a light across the cabin the path of the light beam is easy to see as it hits the dust particles. We are going to imagine right now that light travels a lot more slowly than it does in reality. At the beginning of this experiment the cabin is not accelerated. The light beam travels in a straight line across the cabin. Now the rocket fires. What happens to the path of the beam of light? To follow its course you must look at Figure 10–3. We have drawn reference lines invisible to the passenger to show where the beam is at equal intervals. During the first period the rocket floor has begun to move up and, as the drawing shows, the light beam hits our first mark at *a,* closer to the floor than was its starting point. During the second interval the floor moves up still farther and the light beam hits the second mark at *b*. By the time the light reaches the third mark the floor intersects the beam. This is how *we* see the situation, but the man in the cabin sees it quite differently. He thinks that the light beam is bent; in his reference system it *is* bent. In our reference system the light has moved in a straight line. If light can be bent in an accelerated system, then so can it be bent by gravity!

We should confess that the amount of bending is greatly exaggerated in our drawing in order to show the effect. The speed of light is actually so great that in traversing such a short distance as the width of a cabin it would scarcely be bent at all. Certainly the astronaut could not notice this deflection. The amount of bending of a light beam by gravity is very small, which explains why it was not observed until scientists began to look for this phenomenon. The angular deflection α of a beam of light at a distance R from the center of a body of mass M is

$$\alpha = \frac{4GM}{c^2R}.$$

(The angle α is expressed in radians; there are 2π radians in a circle, so a radian equals $360/2\pi$ or 57.3 degrees. G is the gravitational constant, and c is the velocity of light.) The deflection caused by the sun should be 1.75 seconds of arc, not very much when you remember that there are 3600 seconds in a degree. Because the sun is so bright we are usually unable to see starlight passing near it, bent or unbent. Only when the bright disk of the sun is obscured, during a rare solar eclipse, can we check whether or not starlight is deflected by the sun. This is done by photographing the positions of stars whose light passes near the edge of the sun during the eclipse. These photographs are compared with others taken six months earlier when the sun appears to be in the opposite side of the sky and the light from these same stars would suffer the least deflection. If the starlight is indeed bent as it passes near the sun, then the apparent positions of the stars shift. The observations that have been made do show a deflection of approximately the amount predicted by the general theory, but there have been too few eclipses to give enough data to provide a wholly clear-cut proof that Einstein was right.

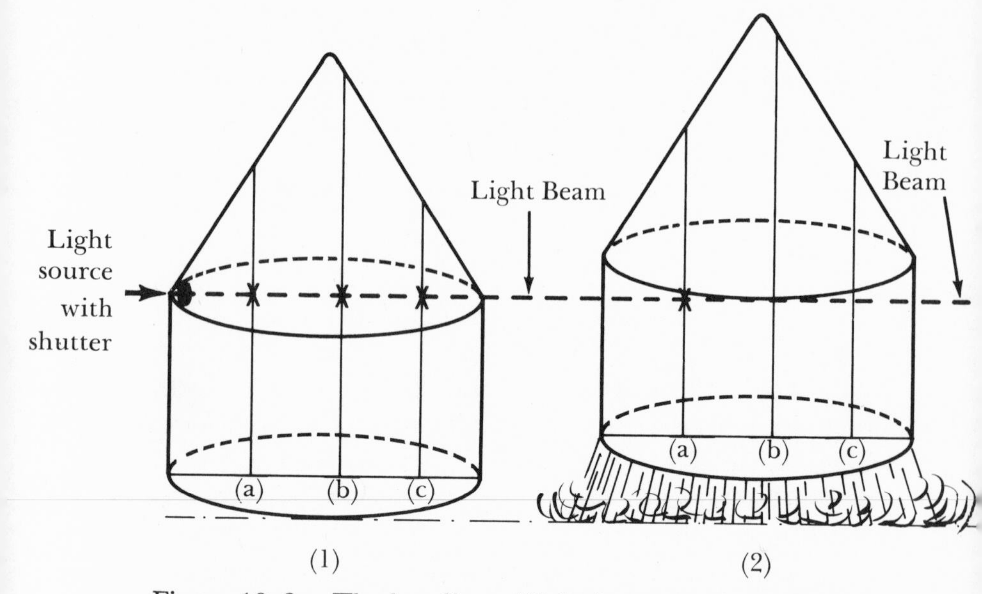

Figure 10–3. The bending of light in an accelerated reference system. The lines (a), (b), and (c) represent transparent screens on which the position of the light beam is marked.

(1) The rocket is not accelerated. A light beam travels straight and unbent across the cabin.

(2) The rocket fires and is accelerated. A light beam transmitted at the time of firing will move in a straight line *in our reference system* and will arrive at screen (a) when the rocket is at position (2). Meanwhile the rocket has moved up so that the light beam hits screen (a) at the point marked,

Another attempt to verify the general theory was reported on recently by physicists at the Massachusetts

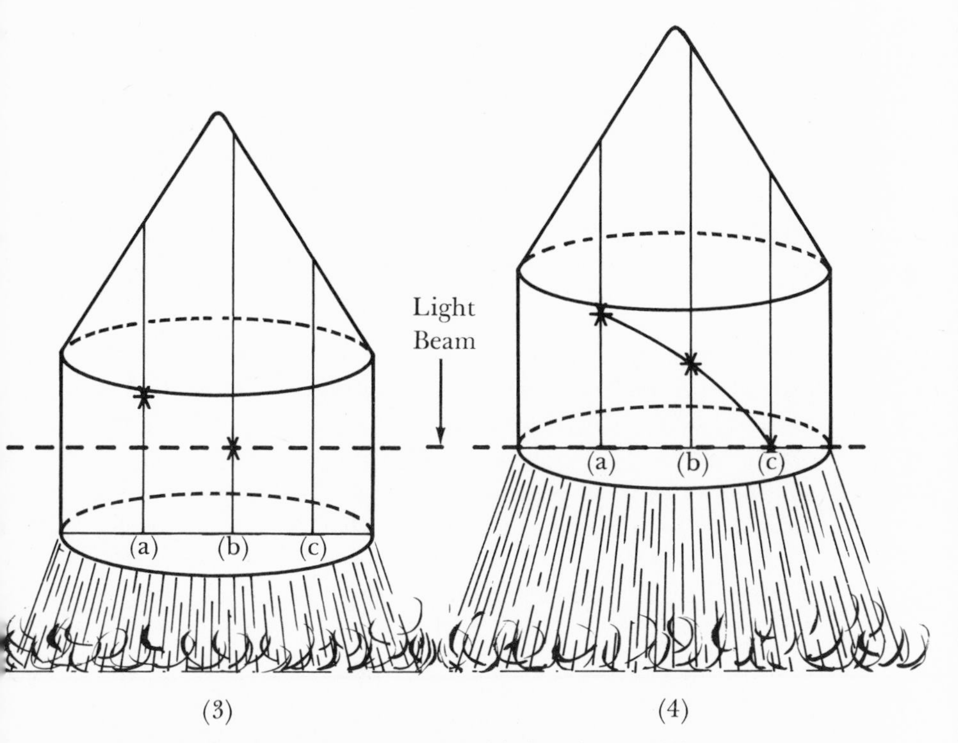

(3) (4)

closer to the floor than where it hit in picture (1).

(3) The light beam continues to move in a straight line as we see it and hits screen (b) at a point closer to the floor than where it hit screen (a) because the floor moved up.

(4) When the light beam arrives at screen (c) the rocket has moved up so much that the floor is at the level of the light beam, as we see the situation from outside the space cabin. A person inside would join the points marked on the screens, see that the curve is a parabola, and conclude that light is bent into a parabolic curve in an accelerated system.

Institute of Technology. During two periods when the sun lay between the earth and Mercury, radar waves were bounced off this planet. See Figure 10–4. The expected bending of these waves as they passed near the sun would produce a longer path for the waves to travel and would lengthen the time needed to make the trip by the amount, if Einstein's theory were correct, of one five-thousandth of a second. Despite great difficulties in measuring the very weak return signal the scientists

Figure 10–4. The bending of an electromagnetic wave by the gravitational field of the sun. A radar wave beamed at Mercury when it is near the sun is bent by the effect of the sun's gravity. The time needed for the wave to travel this lengthened path is greater than it would be to travel an unbent path to Mercury and back. The preliminary results of the measurement of this time delay agree well with that predicted by Einstein's general theory of relativity.

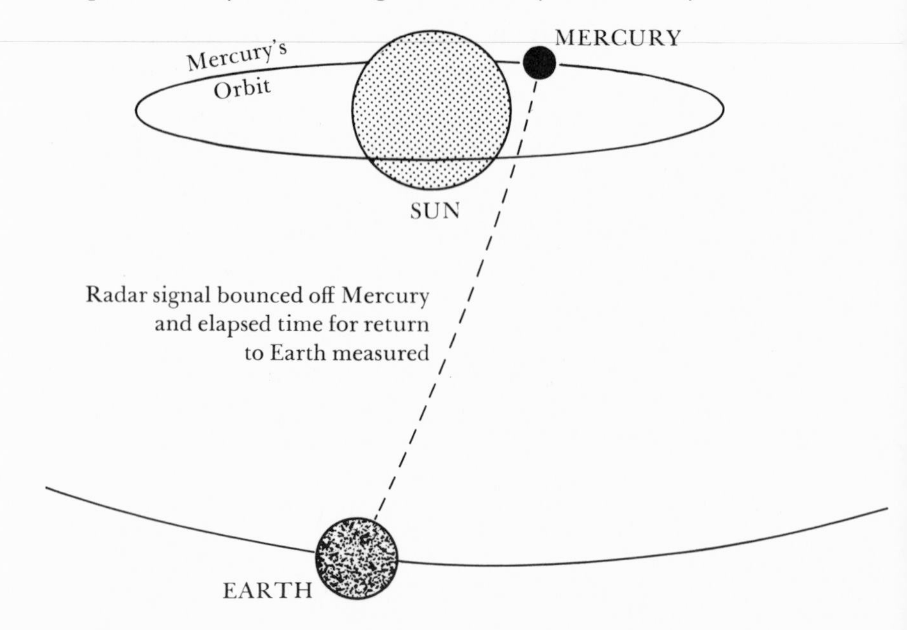

did succeed in determining this delay, which was in fact about one five-thousandth of a second just before Mercury passed behind the sun. Because the accuracy of this preliminary test was only about 20 percent the results are not yet regarded as conclusive, but improvements in technique should soon make it possible to tell once and for all whether or not electromagnetic waves are bent in a gravitational field.

The bending of light by gravity may provide the explanation for the existence of those celestial oddities known as *quasars.* The puzzling thing about quasars is that they are *too* bright. No one has provided a satisfactory answer to the question of where the energy comes from to make quasars give off so much electromagnetic radiation. An interesting suggestion made very recently is that quasars are not after all extra bright. They may be ordinary galaxies shining with a normal luminosity, whose light rays have been bent and focused by the presence of a very massive body, perhaps a second galaxy, lying between us and the quasar. The second galaxy would act as a lens to concentrate the light from the quasar and make it appear much brighter than it really is. The magnification could be as great as 300,000 million!

Gravitational Red Shift

A massive body not only bends light, it also can change its frequency in an effect known as the *gravitational red shift.* A photon leaves the surface of the body with a certain energy hf. It uses up energy in fighting its way free of the body's gravitational field, and so when it escapes it has a lower energy hf' and a lower frequency f'. "Down" in frequency means a shift toward the red end of the spectrum, which accounts for the name of this effect. This gravitational red shift should not be confused with the *Doppler red shift* which occurs in light emitted from an object moving away from the observer, much as the pitch of a train whistle changes as the train approaches and recedes.

Scientists have looked for evidence of the gravitational red shift which by its presence or absence can provide a badly needed check on the general theory of relativity. This shift was observed in light from the very massive stars known as white dwarfs. A more precise measurement of this shift has been obtained in the laboratory. The very high frequency electromagnetic waves called gamma waves were allowed to "fall" through a distance of several meters, and a frequency shift was observed which agreed with Einstein's prediction.

Warping of Space

Once physicists defined a straight line as the path followed by a beam of light in a vacuum. How does the discovery that light is bent in the presence of gravity affect this definition? Einstein's interpretation was that space itself is warped in the region around a massive object, so that light does in fact follow the shortest path between two points on the curved surface of space. As you know, the shortest distance between two points on a globe does not appear as a straight line between these same points on an ordinary flat map. Instead this "straight line" distance is projected as a segment of the earth's radius called a "great circle." In the same way light, which is pursuing a straight course in the space which is warped, appears to follow a curved path when it is projected into our world.

Gravitons

One of the predictions of Einstein's general theory of relativity is that accelerated masses should emit gravitational waves just as accelerated electric charges are the source of electromagnetic waves. And, just as the electromagnetic radiation is quantized into particles called photons, so may these gravitational waves be quantized into particles called *gravitons.* So far, neither gravitational waves nor gravitons have been observed. Because the gravitational force is so small compared with, for example, the electric force of attraction between charged bodies, detection of gravitational waves and gravitons is no easy matter. Nevertheless, they may some day be found to exist.

This is the end of our story of gravity, a tale that is even now not complete. Einstein was unable to bring his theory to a satisfactory conclusion, unable to answer many of the questions he raised. Despite the work of many theoretical physicists, the theory of gravity has hardly advanced since Einstein's time. We are left strangely uneasy, taunted by unanswered questions. Is it possible that we shall never be sure what, if any, connection exists between gravitation and electromagnetism and that we shall never know how a gravitational force is transmitted from one body to another? It is more likely that a clue will appear from some unexpected source—from some other field of study perhaps. Working from such a clue, theoretical physicists may be able to give new life to the study of gravity and arrive at last at a unified theory of gravitation and electromagnetism.

chapter eleven

ALL THE MATHEMATICS YOU NEED TO KNOW TO UNDERSTAND THIS BOOK

1. Notation and Mathematical Terms

In the language of mathematics various symbols have been agreed upon to mean that certain mathematical operations are to be performed. You may already know many or all of these symbols; in any case you may find the following "translation" into English helpful. The definitions are illustrated by typical examples.

MULTIPLICATION

$(2)(a)$	means	2 times a.
$2a$	means	2 times a.
$b(2a)$ or $(2a)b$	means	2 times a times b.
$2(a + b)$	means	$2a + 2b$, or 2 times a plus 2 times b.
$2(a - b)$	means	$2a - 2b$, or 2 times a minus 2 times b.
3×10^2	means	3 times 10 squared (the "$\times$" means "times" and is used only before numbers with exponents in this book).

DIVISION

$\frac{a}{b}$	means	a divided by b.
a/b	means	a divided by b.
$\frac{a+b}{2}$	means	the sum of a plus b divided by 2, which is the same as $a/2 + b/2$.
$\frac{a-b}{2}$	means	$a/2 - b/2$.

EXPONENTS

$a^1 = a$.
$a^2 =$ a times a = a squared.
$a^3 =$ a times a times a = a cubed.
$a^4 =$ a times a times a times a = a to the fourth power, and so on.

$a^{1/2} = \sqrt{a}$ is called the square root of a.
$a^{1/3} = \sqrt[3]{a}$ is called the cube root of a.
$a^{1/4} = \sqrt[4]{a}$ is called the fourth root of a, and so on.

$a^{-1} = 1/a^1 = 1/a$ is called the reciprocal of a.
$a^{-2} = 1/a^2$ is called the inverse square of a.
$a^{-3} = 1/a^3$ is called the inverse cube of a.
$a^{-4} = 1/a^4$ is called the inverse fourth power of a, and so on.

WORKING WITH EXPONENTS

To multiply a number such as a which is raised to some power (a number that has an exponent) by the same number raised to a power, you *add* the exponents as shown below. It may seem odd to you to add in order to multiply, but the following examples should convince you as well as illustrate the procedure that is followed.

$a^2 \times a^3 = (a \times a)(a \times a \times a) = a \times a \times a \times a \times a = a^5.$

If $a = 2$, you can verify this statement by substitution:
$2^2 \times 2^3 = (4)(8) = 32$
while $2^5 = 2 \times 2 \times 2 \times 2 \times 2 = 32.$

$a^3 \times a^{-1} = a^2$ (because $3 + (-1) = 2$).

You can verify this by substitution; for example, try $a = 3$.
$3 \times 3 \times 3 \times \frac{1}{3} = 9 = 3^2.$

$a^{1/2} \times a^{1/2} = a^1 = a.$
If $a = 9$, $a^{1/2} = 3$, and so $a^{1/2} \times a^{1/2} = 3 \times 3 = 9 = a.$

To divide numbers with exponents you subtract the exponent of the divisor from that of the dividend as shown.

$\dfrac{a^5}{a^3} = a^2$ $\qquad$ $\dfrac{a^6}{a^4} = a^2$

$\dfrac{a^{1/2}}{a^{1/4}} = a^{1/4}$ $\qquad$ $\dfrac{a^{-8}}{a^{-10}} = a^2$

$\dfrac{a^6}{a^{-4}} = a^{10}$

When raising a number with an exponent to a higher power you *multiply* the exponents.

$$(a^3)^2 = a^{(3 \times 2)} = a^6$$

You can see that this must be so by simply writing out the terms as follows:

$$(a^3)^2 = (a \times a \times a)(a \times a \times a) = a \times a \times a \times a \times a \times a = a^6.$$

POWERS OF TEN

The letter a in the examples above can stand for any number, but in our decimal system we find it very convenient to use powers of $a = 10$ to express very large and very small numbers as follows:

$10^0 = 1$
$10^1 = 10$
$10^2 = 100$
$10^3 = 1{,}000$
$10^4 = 10{,}000$
$10^5 = 100{,}000$
$10^6 = 1{,}000{,}000 = 1$ million
$10^7 = 10{,}000{,}000$
$10^8 = 100{,}000{,}000$
$10^9 = 1{,}000{,}000{,}000 = 1$ billion
$10^{-1} = 1/10 = .1$
$10^{-2} = 1/100 = .01$
$10^{-3} = 1/1000 = .001$

and so on.

A large number can be expressed by the appropriate power of ten times some multiplier, for example:

$3{,}100 = 3.1 \times 10^3 = 3.1$ thousands
$62{,}500 = 6.25 \times 10^4 = 6.25$ ten-thousands
$7{,}012{,}000 = 7.012 \times 10^6 = 7.012$ million
$.0015 = 1.5 \times 10^{-3} = 1.5$ thousandths

SUBSCRIPTS

Subscripts are used to label quantities and are written like this: T_1, T_2, T_3, or v_x, v_y. Notice that the subscripts are always *under* the line ("sub" means under) and so they cannot be confused with the exponents which are above the line.

RATIO

The ratio of two numbers is the quotient of the first divided by the second. The ratio of a to b is a/b.

PROPORTIONALITY

If two variable quantities x and y are so related that doubling x doubles y, tripling x triples y, halving x halves y, and so on, then we say that x is *directly proportional* to y. We can write that $x = cy$, or $x/y = c$, where c is called the constant of proportionality. You can see from the latter equation that if you double x you must also double y for c to remain the same.

A different situation occurs when one variable is directly proportional to some *power* of the other variable. An example of this came on page 51 of this book. The distance d fallen by a body was proportional to the time of falling squared, or to t^2. If we double d, to maintain the equation $d/t^2 = k$ we have to multiply t, not by 2, but by $\sqrt{2}$.

A third situation arises when as one variable increases, the other decreases. This is called inverse proportionality. A simple case occurs when doubling one variable halves the other, tripling one variable divides the other in three, quadrupling one variable divides the other in four, and so on. This would be expressed as $a = C/b$ where C is a constant. The type of inverse proportionality that you will meet most often in this book is inverse *square* proportionality. In this type of relationship $a = K/b^2$. In our case on page 75 the mutual force F of gravitational attraction between two bodies whose centers are a distance r apart is $F = m_1m_2G/r^2$. The variable F depends on the inverse square of the variable r. The constant is made up of three constants multiplied together, m_1; m_2; and G.

2. *Algebra*

Algebra is based on the equality between two sides of an "equation." The key thing to remember in performing operations in algebra is that the two sides of the equation must remain forever in balance. What you do to one side you must do to the other side, treating both with complete impartiality.

Solving for an unknown, which is usually written as a letter, is done by carrying out various operations on an equation with the aim of getting the unknown to stand *alone* on one side of the equation while the rest of the numbers and symbols are on the other side. Although this procedure can be very difficult at times, in this book the solutions are all easy. Various examples of simple equations and how they are solved follow.

SOLUTION BY SUBTRACTION

$$a + 15 = 30$$
$$a + 15 - 15 = 30 - 15$$
$$a + 0 = 15$$
$$a = 15.$$

Subtract 15 from each side of the equation.

SOLUTION BY ADDITION

$$b - 7.5 = 6.5$$
$$b - 7.5 + 7.5 = 6.5 + 7.5$$
$$b = 14.$$

Add 7.5 to each side of the equation.

SOLUTION BY DIVISION

$$30c = 60$$

Divide each side by 30.

$$\frac{30}{30}c = \frac{60}{30}$$
$$c = 2.$$

SOLUTION BY MULTIPLICATION

$$\frac{d}{10} = 9$$ Multiply each side by 10.

$$\left(\frac{d}{10}\right)10 = (9)\ (10)$$

$$d = 90.$$

SOLUTION BY SQUARING

$$\sqrt{x} = 9$$ Square both sides of the equation.

$$x = (9)\ (9)$$

$$x = 81.$$

SOLUTION BY COMBINATIONS OF THESE

$$y + 22 = 12y$$ Collect all the y's on the same side by subtracting y from each side.

$$22 = 12y - y$$

$$22 = 11y$$ Divide each side by 11.

$$y = 2.$$

$$\frac{z - 10}{5} = 25$$ Multiply throughout by 5.

$$z - 10 = 125$$ Add 10 to each side.

$$z = 135.$$

$$9\,\frac{(a + 1)}{15} = 12a$$ Multiply each side by 15.

$$9(a + 1) = 180a$$ Divide each side by 9.

$$a + 1 = 20a$$ Collect the a's by subtracting a from each side.

$$1 = 19a$$

$$a = \frac{1}{19}.$$

CROSS-MULTIPLYING

$\frac{A}{B} = \frac{C}{D}$ Multiply both sides by B.

$A = \frac{BC}{D}$ Multiply both sides by D.

$AD = BC$ You can see that this result is the same as if you had multiplied across the original equation, as shown at the left. Cross-multiplying saves steps and time in solving equations of two ratios.

$\frac{A}{B} \times \frac{C}{D}$

INDEX